ASK THE EX

72 EQUINE PROBLEMS SOLVED

A HORSE'S MOUTH PUBLICATION

First published in Great Britain in 2002
© **D J Murphy (Publishers) Ltd**
The Horse's Mouth is a subsidiary of
D J Murphy (Publishers) Ltd

Editor: **Janet Rising**
Designer: **Jamie Powell**
Published by **D J Murphy (Publishers) Ltd,**
Haslemere House, Lower Street, Haslemere,
Surrey GU27 2PE.
Origination by **Ford Graphics Ltd**, Ringwood,
Hampshire.
Printed by **The Grange Press**, Brighton,
West Sussex.
Front cover image: **David Miller.**

ISBN 0-9513707-5-8

Ask the Experts appears every month in
HORSE&RIDER magazine.

Many of the photographs in this book were staged
and specially taken, and the publishers would like
to make clear that the horses and ponies depicted
may not necessarily suffer from the problems
featured.

ASK THE EXPERTS

MEET THE EXPERTS

Rob Pilsworth MA, VetMB, CertVR, BSc, MRCVS qualified from Cambridge University School of Veterinary Medicine in 1981. He spent five years in mixed practice before joining Rossdale & Partners, in Newmarket, in 1986. He became a partner in the practice two years later. He has particular interests in diagnostic imaging and lameness diagnosis.

Fliss Gillott BHSII, BHSI (SM), NPSD started riding at the age of two and was brought up with horses which completely took over her family's farm. Fliss went through Pony Club and Riding Club activities and developed a lasting passion for dressage. She still teaches riding for a living and is reading Psychology with the Open University.

Dr Natalie Waran is a lecturer in animal behaviour and welfare at the University of Edinburgh and is also the Director of the Postgraduate Masters course in behaviour and welfare. Her main interest is horse behaviour and she writes for scientific and consumer journals. She lives in Scotland with her family and various animals, including three Thoroughbred horses, and is a keen amateur competitor - when time allows!

Jane van Lennep MSc, NPSD, BHS SM also started out on the family farm/riding school. After qualifying, Jane ran a training stud/livery yard for 21 years and now breeds and competes with Endurance Arabs. Jane's approach to horse management is an holistic one, and constantly refers to nature and natural methods. Jane has written two books and she and Fliss have answered readers' equine problems in HORSE&RIDER magazine since 1983.

Sara Wyche MRCVS worked in Germany as a successful professional musician before changing horses midstream to study veterinary medicine. She qualified in 1986 from Giessen University. During 11 years spent in Germany, she met several practitioners experienced in the field of alternative medicine, as well as riding for a strict dressage trainer. A fascination with the horse's movement and a desire to understand problems in gait and coordination led her toward a career in equine rehabilitation. She takes an holistic approach to treatment and has written four books on different aspects of the horse's musculoskeletal system.

Richard Chamberlain LL.B (Hons), TEP, Solicitor is a partner in the firm of Swayne Johnson & Wright Solicitors of St Asaph, Denbighshire, and is a member of the Equine Lawyers Association. He has many years experience of dealing with horse-related legal problems, and is the Company Secretary and legal adviser of the Appaloosa Horse Club (UK) Ltd. He learnt to ride at the age of 10 and has been breeding, breaking and showing his own Appaloosa horses since 1989.

Contents

Going straight

"HELP! I HAVE A REAL PROBLEM RIDING MY HORSE IN A STRAIGHT LINE."

Q In a dressage test my horse is more likely to enter at C and wiggle down the centre line rather than go straight. Any suggestions?

A Horses do not naturally move in straight lines. You only have to look at the tracks made by horses on old pasture to see this. Meandering at slow speed is part of the horse's genetic make up. On the other hand, a fast moving horse takes a much straighter line as this will give him the quickest route to his destination or out of danger.

With this knowledge, it is easy to see why impulsion is necessary to produce a straight line from the ridden horse. The two words 'forward' and 'straight' are so intertwined that you cannot truly have one without the other. Bear in mind that 'impulsion' is a desire to move forward, and not speed, although speed may be incorporated in impulsion.

Born one-sided

People are no more straight than horses. We are all, with few exceptions, born either right or left handed and this affects our ability to ride straight. There is plenty that can be done off the horse to remedy the situation and to build the strength in the weaker side.

Remember to groom equally with left and right hands, however awkward it may feel, to swap the yard broom from side to side, and to lift bales of hay using either knee to get the lift into the wheelbarrow - all these things will ultimately be of help in getting your horse straight once in the saddle.

Even if you are obliged to spend your day sitting at a desk in front of a computer you can make an effort to sit equally on your seat bones, and to have a straight back rather than

flopping to one side or the other with your legs crossed under the desk.

If you are having difficulty riding a straight line, the first step is to think forward and straight. Target a point in the distance which is beyond where you want to make your next turn. Each time you make a turn, find a new target. Ride in that direction with enthusiasm which will then be transmitted to your horse. The advantage of having a target beyond the corner is that you avoid a collapse before the corner - mentally you have never quite arrived, and so you are less likely to be tempted to stop riding forward.

Imagining that you have a jump in front of you is a useful way of focusing your mind on riding forward and straight without rushing. If you use this trick, it helps to put your jump outside the arena!

Finally, imagine that you are riding along tram lines so that you are riding between the two lines. Your left leg and hand contains the left side, and your right leg and hand contains the right side.

Using the correct aids

The way you use your weight and apply the aids is what, in the end, results in the horse being straight or otherwise. The more responsive the horse is to the aids the straighter he is likely to be. When you increase the pressure with your leg, he should respond, and when you close your fingers on the reins he should respond to that too. When this is the case, as long as you ride every stride forward, and clearly direct each stride, you will have a straight horse.

The more quickly you are able to respond to a change in your horse's balance, the less will be the deviation from a straight line. In a fenced arena, the horse's tendency will be to collapse to the inside. Increased pressure from your inside leg, supported by a steady contact on the outside rein, will successfully keep the horse out and straight.

Some practical exercises

Place pairs of cones in straight lines about 10m apart. It is much easier to hold a straight line over a short distance than a long one, so use your markers to work on riding a straight line over 20, 30 and eventually up to 40 to 60 metres.

Riding transitions on these straight lines will help to confirm straightness and will also give you much better transitions. If you are still having problems, try lengthening the stride to improve impulsion, working from one pair of cones to another before shortening again.

Include circle work before and after a straight line, with changes of direction to help you get the feel of riding forward from a turn.

Correcting crookedness

It must always be remembered that a horse will try to stay under the rider's weight. Unless you sit straight, your horse will always be crooked. We all need help from time to time with this one because feeling straight does not necessarily equate to being straight. Your horse will try his best to tell you if you are crooked, but somebody on the ground will be able to tell you in what way you are crooked.

Using your weight to ride a turn, by shifting your weight in the required direction, will result in more subtle aids and leave you in a much better position to ride forward and straight from a turn.

An ability to ride straight will develop through constant vigilance. Just as a green horse needs teaching to work forward in a straight line before he does it instinctively, so does the rider. The more you work at it the easier it becomes!
Fliss Gillott

Conditioning without fizz

"WHAT CAN I FEED TO KEEP MY THOROUGHBRED MARE SANE?"

Q **I purchased my Thoroughbred mare when she was in very poor condition at the age of three-and-a-half years old.**

With good feeding, her condition has improved dramatically but she is quite lively to ride, so I have cut her feed down.

In summer I was able to keep her on good grazing balanced with a little extra hard feed; this kept her calm and looking well. How can I keep her sane but still keep the condition on her over the winter?

A It is very interesting that you observed how well your mare looked and how much better her temperament was when she was out to grass full time and not getting any extra feeding. You have proved to yourself that grazing is the best feed for horses. After all, it is what they evolved to eat!

Many Thoroughbreds are not good doers because they have been bred for many generations to mature quickly and go fast as two-year-olds. However, you are lucky, as it does not seem that your mare is a bad doer.

She is now in good order. She will never again need the same level of feeding that it took to achieve this, because she has more or less finished growing now. You are right to consider a feeding plan which mimics summer grazing and contains less hard feed.

A natural diet

The summer grass was full of vitamins, minerals, protein and good quality fibre. It is possible to create a winter feed which is similarly high in these nutrients. Cereals, which are the basis of most cubes and mixes, are high in starches, but generally low in vitamins, minerals (except phosphorus) and fibre.

Obviously, good quality hay is going to be the basis of your winter feeding. Really nice meadow hay will be best of all. Boost your hay with some alfalfa hay, if possible.

For your manger feed, consider sugar beet (high in digestible fibre and calcium), alfalfa pellets, high in vitamin A, protein and calcium), grass pellets (less protein and more carbohydrate than alfalfa), and AlfaBeet (an unmolassed blend of sugar beet and alfalfa).

I have successfully fed up to 3kg dry weight a day of sugar beet, and frequently use 2kg per horse per day. It makes an excellent, juicy and bulky base feed to which you can add other ingredients as necessary. Build up gradually over one or two weeks. The horse will eat it slowly, more like the natural grazing pattern of feeding which helps to prevent boredom as well as being much better for the horse.

To this, you could add alfalfa or grass nuts. The grass nuts are a little higher in energy, but the alfalfa is higher in calcium, which I think might be better for your mare.

Supplements

This diet will be naturally high in vitamins and minerals, so you may well feel that your supplements are not now needed. If you wish to continue with them, it might be a good idea to check with your vet that they are, in fact, necessary and that they are appropriate to her needs now.

If you want to continue the theme that 'natural is best' you might prefer to use a seaweed supplement for extra vitamins and minerals.

Should your mare need more feed value in winter, and you do not want to risk her getting above herself on traditional mixes or cereals, then you can add a high oil feed to her diet. Oil is well tolerated by horses and, like fibrous feeds, provides a slow release of energy.

You may prefer not to use a refined oil, but a whole oil seed. The traditional feed here has always been linseed, which has gone out of favour because it is a bind to soak, simmer and boil before it is safe to feed, but you can now get ready to feed, full fat linseed meal, such as Simple System Instant Linseed or Hilton Herbs Linseed and Fenugreek.

Do not clip off more of your mare's coat than is necessary - a bib or apron clip will suffice. If you ride for one-and-a-half hours, you may feel you do not want her coat on for that time, but what about the other 22^1/2 hours when your horse might think that a coat would be nice? Even a small clip includes the throat and belly - rugs don't cover these areas, so can never make up for the lost coat.

Jane van Lennep

12

Travel trauma

"HOW CAN I HELP MY HORSE TO TRAVEL WELL? HE'S TERRIFIED."

Q I have to take my two horses from the Shetland Islands down to mainland Scotland to begin our journey to our new home in West Yorkshire. The ferry journey is 14 hours long, but they will have to be loaded four hours prior to departure. However, one of my horses travels extremely badly – he panics and gets claustrophobic when he's in the trailer. What's more, he has a pathological hatred of vets – having suffered an accident when he got his hindlegs stuck in a wire fence, he panicked when he came round from the anaesthetic and tried to climb out of the stable. I am extremely worried about doing this long journey – what do you suggest I do?

A First and foremost, do you have adequate safety precautions in place? Is the trailer/horse box sufficiently padded? Do you have contingency plans in case of an emergency?

Have you made the ferry operators aware that your horse may become very distressed during the journey? Do you have the correct insurance in the event of your trailer – or your horse – causing damage to persons or property while on board the ferry? As much as he hates vets, the thought of this horse injuring himself severely during the sea crossing – and having to wait until the ferry docks before his suffering is relieved – doesn't bear thinking about. So have you asked a veterinary practice, local to the ferry terminal, to be on standby?

Many horses are afraid of vets and veterinary treatment, because the treatment inevitably takes place at a time when the horse is at his most vulnerable – for example, when he is, literally, a wounded animal. Equally, such emergency situations are extremely stressful for the owner, because they present a catalogue of uncertainties – uncertain prognosis, uncertain expectations of treatment and so on.

Homeopathy can help

When both horse and owner suddenly find themselves being star players in an unrehearsed drama, it is not surprising that emotions like fear, anger and suspicion are aroused – and that, with hindsight, these become inextricably linked to the presence of a third party, usually the vet. Nevertheless, when faced with a horse in pain and panic owners should remind themselves that it takes considerable courage to deal with an animal, once it is in distress.

Although chemical sedation is not appropriate for your horse on the intended journey, there are other ways of helping him to overcome his terror. High-potency (homeopathic) Aconite would probably be the most reliable and a course of Rescue Remedy might be introduced prior to the journey. And have you thought of using Skullcap and Valerian - herbs which promote drowsiness?

Also, encourage your horse to drink as much water as possible during the 24 hours prior to the journey – you could do this by temporarily increasing his intake of electrolytes. This would also help his body to combat the stress of travelling. And electrolytes should, of course, be administered immediately after the voyage.

Given that your horse has had a wrenching injury to the hindlegs, are you sure his fear of the trailer is really caused by the feeling of being shut in? When a horse gets caught up in a fence, it is almost impossible for him to free his hindlegs without pulling his back. Together with the bad recovery from the subsequent anaesthetic, he is almost certain to have pulled muscles, probably along the lumbar spine. Most horses are then usually terrified to travel in a trailer because they instinctively know that they are unable to keep their balance. On a sea crossing, this lack of balance would be made more acute.

Are all eventualities covered?

This journey should not be made unless you have people in place to cover every worst-case scenario – whether they be vets, port authorities or simply trusted friends. You might also consider enlisting the additional help of a radionics specialist. They would be able to support the horse's mental well-being in the form of 'distant healing'. But do, please, remember that no practitioner and no form of therapy can entirely safeguard your horse on this hazardous journey. The ultimate responsibility lies with you.

Sara Wyche

Bit fitting

"HOW HIGH SHOULD THE BIT BE FITTED IN MY HORSE'S MOUTH?"

Q **I am confused as to how high I should fit the bit in my horse's mouth, and does it differ when fitting a straight bar or a jointed bit?**

A Before looking at how bits are fitted it is important to remember that each horse is unique, not only in size and shape of mouth but also in temperament and sensitivity. You will develop a feel for what is right with experience, responding to the way the horse works and the feel he gives you from his mouth. Having said all that, there are a few simple guidelines which one can follow.

The height of the bit in the mouth is taken from its position in the corners of the lips. In other words, viewed without opening the mouth, how much does the bit make the horse 'smile?' With a jointed bit, it is advisable to hold the sides of the bit down from the front, by hooking a finger of each hand over the visible ends of the mouthpiece, before making a final

judgement on whether or not the height is correct. When correctly fitted, the bit should just crinkle the corners of the mouth.

If a bit is fitted too low, there is a greater danger of the horse getting his tongue over it. Even without this happening, a low bit will be sloppy and uncomfortable and more likely to cause bruising, especially if it comes into contact with the tushes or teeth.

If the cheekpieces bulge when you take up a contact, the bit is too low. Fitting the bit too high in the mouth will lead to rubbing and pinching at the corners of the mouth. Sometimes this is necessary in the short term to correct a tendency to put the tongue over. In this case, it is kinder not to work for long enough to cause discomfort and certainly not for so long that the bit starts to rub.
Fliss Gillott

To buy, or not to buy?

"SHOULD I BUY A HORSE WITH FOOT PROBLEMS?"

Q I have been leasing a horse with an option to buy. The owner is asking for quite a substantial sum for her so I have had her vetted. Unfortunately she failed the examination due to sidebone on one of her forelegs and a bone chip on the fetlock. She also has upright pasterns and boxy front feet. Are any of these conditions likely to cause her problems in the future?

A The fact that a horse fails a veterinary examination does not mean it is unsuitable for purchase. What your veterinary surgeon is doing, in examining the horse, is assessing all of the lesions and abnormalities in that horse, and giving an opinion, which is his personal opinion, over whether those problems will bother the horse in the future.

Many horses which have failed a veterinary examination will go on to perform very successfully for many years. I have the rare distinction of having failed a horse as a two-year-old which went on to win the Derby! However, this horse had fragments of bone visible on its radiographs which would have made it impossible to pass him without risking a negligence claim should the horse have gone lame subsequently.

The veterinary surgeon who examined your mare is in the same position in that she clearly has a bone chip in one fetlock which could eventually lead to lameness. He is only doing his job by alerting you to this abnormality, and would find it very difficult to pass the horse unequivocally in the face of such a lesion.

Correcting abnormalities
Upright pasterns and boxy feet don't always lead to problems, but in my experience they are often linked to suspensory desmitis and sesamoid problems.

I would definitely not try to correct boxy feet. The horse has got used to these feet over the years and the forces on the tendons and suspensory apparatus will be finely tuned to accommodate the horse's conformation.

It is a great temptation to lower the heels and make these feet look better, but this will almost certainly lead to problems as the horse will lose the support in the back of the leg and will probably develop either a bowed tendon or suspensory desmitis as a consequence.

Taking a risk
My own view is that if you like the mare and you are prepared to take a risk, go ahead and buy her. Every horse has a value of some sort, and with a horse with these kind of problems, it may simply be a case of negotiating to find a price which is acceptable to you and the vendor, with the inherent degree of risk that it may not remain sound.

Where you may get into difficulty is if you wish to insure the horse for full loss of use after purchase. Most insurance companies would quite reasonably take the view that they would not be prepared to give loss of use cover on a horse with abnormalities which could cause lameness in the future.

Rob Pilsworth

Disunited canter

"IS THERE A CONNECTION BETWEEN MY MARE'S SPAVIN AND HER GOING DISUNITED?"

Q **My mare has a spavin on her right hind and often goes disunited in right canter. Could there be a connection?**

A It is almost certain that your mare is feeling some discomfort from her hock. It would be too much of a coincidence for her to have difficulty in canter to the right when she has a spavin on the right, for there not to be a connection. It is also more than likely that she has developed a back problem as a direct result of being unable to use the off hind as it should be used. Going disunited in canter is a classic sign of discomfort in the sacro-iliac region, which a good equitherapist should be able to remedy.

The hock, on the other hand, may be an ongoing problem. If your equitherapist is also a physiotherapist, he or she would be the best person to give you advice as to beneficial exercise for the affected joint. It is unlikely to be anything treatable, other than through correct work, and there is also the added potential problem that hock number two will go the same way. Spavins are generally the result of a weakness in the joint and hereditary predisposition to develop an unsoundness. However, the fact that the mare is apparently sound in every other way suggests that the problem is minor and need not affect her performance for normal work. If you had ambitions to take her to Grand Prix level, or to event her, then you might have to think again!

If your mare develops anything more than slight discomfort on one canter, it would be advisable to call in the vet so that you can get an accurate diagnosis of what is going on inside the joint. In the meantime, however, with appropriate treatment from a physiotherapist, there is no reason why you should not be able to overcome this current tendency to disunite in canter.

Fliss Gillott

Is the yard liable?

"SHOULD I SIGN A DISCLAIMER?"

Q **My livery yard has asked me to sign a disclaimer so that any injury caused to my horse while on the yard will not be their fault. My horse and I are very happy there, but I am concerned about the barbed-wire fencing, which is in a bad state of repair. Plus, there's an unsociable gelding who could feasibly chase my horse into the fencing. Does the proprietor have a 'duty of care' should anything happen?**

A Any agreement between you and the owner of the livery yard is a contract for the provision of services. In return for the payment of the appropriate fee, the owner of the livery yard agrees to provide shelter, grazing and a degree of general care of the horse placed in his care. The amount of care provided will depend upon the terms of the contract. Full livery will clearly involve a high degree of care including feeding, turnout, exercise and general supervision. DIY livery, on the other hand, may involve the yard owner in no more than the provision of the basic facilities in the form of stabling and turnout area.

You make no reference to any other written terms of your contract with the yard owner and it would appear that the only written document you have been asked to sign is a disclaimer to the effect that the yard owner will not be liable for any injury sustained by her horse. The extent to which such a disclaimer will be effective depends upon the circumstances giving rise to any particular claim.

Duty of care

In the absence of any written disclaimer, the yard owner's liability to customers depends upon any specific terms of the contract and the general common-law duty of care. The court's approach to the common-law duty of care is to balance the degree of risk and the seriousness of the consequences that result from it, against the expense and effort required in order to minimise or eliminate that risk. The greater the risk or seriousness of the consequences, the greater the effort that must be made to reduce such risk.

It is well-known that barbed wire is not really a suitable form of fencing for horses, even when in good condition. Sadly, however, it is not uncommon and, since you are well aware of the existence of such fencing, it is probable that the yard owner would be entitled to rely upon the disclaimer and would thereby avoid any liability in the event of an injury being sustained from the fencing.

The presence of an unsociable and aggressive horse is a complicating factor which clearly increases the risk of injury. Ordinarily, the yard owner would almost certainly have a duty of care to ensure that the risk of injury itself is minimised by providing separated grazing or by arranging the removal of the offending horse. Failure to take such precautionary steps might give rise to liability in the event of an accident but, again, the yard owner will probably be able to rely upon the disclaimer in order to avoid liability.

Practically speaking

You must either persuade the yard owner to improve his fencing and to regulate the turnout regime or accept the risk in injury to your horse resulting from the circumstances at the yard. The only other option open to you is to find alternative livery.

It should also be mentioned that there is some statutory control of the extent to which one party to a contract can exclude or limit his liability to the other under the Unfair Contract Terms Act of 1977. The Act provides that certain contractual provisions are void and of no effect (mainly provisions which seek to exclude liability for personal injury or death caused by negligence or terms which have the effect of negating the main objects of the contract). Other terms can only be relied upon if it was reasonable in the circumstances for such terms to be included in the contract.

In the situation which you describe, it is possible that in the event of an accident, the courts might find that it was unreasonable of the yard owner to include the disclaimer in the contract. However, this will depend on the relative bargaining strength of the yard owner and yourself (which will include the availability of other livery within a reasonable distance), the extent of the disrepair of the fencing and the turnout arrangements generally. On the information provided, however, I suspect that the yard owner will be able to rely upon the disclaimer.

Richard Chamberlain

He's so naughty

"HOW CAN I BREAK MY HORSE'S BAD HABITS"

Q **I desperately need help with my 17-year-old gelding. He has some very nasty habits, such as rearing, bucking and biting both when ridden and in-hand. Although he has improved since I bought him, he is still very unpredictable. He has had a full check up and and there are no physical problems.**

A It is interesting that this horse behaves badly in-hand as well as under saddle. This bears out the evidence that he is not suffering from problems in his back or his mouth. When there is discomfort in these areas, a normally quiet horse will behave in a quite different manner when he is ridden. With your horse, it would seem that he has a general behavioural problem which will need to be corrected both in-hand and under saddle.

Establishing a pecking order

Your horse must understand that biting, kicking and rearing are wrong under any circumstances, and he should feel guilty about doing any of them. You may need to punish him physically occasionally, accompanied by a strong verbal correction, so that if you growl an angry "No!" at him, he knows he must behave.

Physical punishment is a difficult area to address on paper. I am not suggesting that you 'beat him up' and make him afraid of you - this is not a form of acceptable human behaviour toward another living being. However, for a horse to be safe to handle, he must respect you and your personal space.

If you look at the ways in which horses sort out their own pecking order in the field, it often appears to be very violent, but an established herd will be peaceful with virtually no injuries inflicted on each other at all. This is the balance you need to achieve with your gelding.

You are the boss, the herd leader - if he realises this and respects you, he will no longer attempt all this challenging behaviour. After all this time, he will not change completely and will

still challenge from time to time, but a strong word should keep him in his place.

Effective discipline

Combining noise with 'punishment' will increase its effectiveness without having to hit the horse so hard that he is left feeling bruised and afraid. A slap across the chest with a looped lunge rein makes a lovely noise without causing pain. It is a useful way of teaching a horse to keep his distance whether he has barged or tried to bite. Your response has to be instantaneous to work. Delay even a few seconds, and the horse will be confused.

If you can teach him to respect your space, he will be less able to bite or kick and reduce the confrontation. Keep your hands away from his head when you lead him so that he is not aggravated by your close proximity. If he does not want to bite you, you will not have to tell him off.

Teaching basic obedience

Basic obedience is central to handling a difficult horse. If you tell him to go forward he must, whether in-hand or under saddle. The best way to teach this is on the lunge, reinforcing your voice commands so that they will stand alone in different circumstances.

If he backs off on the lunge, you crack the whip, or flick him with the whip if this has not worked. Sooner or later, when you say "Walk on!" he will do it automatically and you can then reward him. He cannot rear if he is walking forwards.

It may seem strange to go back to such a basic level with a 17-year-old horse, but this is probably the only way you will get an improvement. He needs teaching to lead properly as well, and this means taking him out specifically to work on his manners in hand. Short lessons work best - especially if you are

absolutely consistent in the way that you carry these lessons into everything you do with him.

Ride with confidence

The more you become a strong leader, the more confident your horse will become in your judgement that he is safe. When you ride him out, keep him well between hand and leg so that you are constantly telling him exactly where you want him to go and how you want him to go there.

Remind yourself constantly to ride forward and straight. In this way, he will have less opportunity to spot horrors that may or may not be there or to act on them. Use your voice - make it clear when you are pleased and clear when you are angry. Give precise voice

commands when necessary so that you know he understands.

If he makes you afraid, he will be picking up on this and it will add to his own insecurity, so avoid situations which you feel you cannot cope with. Developing a strong seat will help with keeping him forward thinking and add to your confidence that you can ride him through a tricky situation!

You have a lot of work to do with this horse, but no animal is ever too old to improve.
Fliss Gillott

Hay alternatives

"WHAT CAN I FEED IF I CAN'T GET DECENT HAY?"

Q We have recently moved to the New Forest. Our paddock has been grazed by wandering ponies, so our grazing for our own ponies is practically non-existent. I'm going to have to feed them hay for a while, but the quality doesn't seem particularly good. Is there anything else I could use for my 11 annd 29-year-olds, the youngest of which has developed a 'dusty' cough?

A Finding decent hay is often a problem. I can understand your concerns and in your situation, you certainly do not want to use dusty hay. Haylage, of which there are various makes such as Horsehage or Top Score, as well as unbranded products made by individual farmers, might be a solution.

As it is bagged quicker than normal hay is made, more of the nutritive value is preserved, mainly in the form of a higher level of sugars than is found in the equivalent hay. These sugars may cause concern if the recipient is prone to laminitis or tying-up in any form. Being slightly moist, it is easer to eat than hay and does not last as long. However, it is usually very palatable and is dust-free. It has a higher water content than hay, as well as a higher nutritive value, so in practice you would probably substitute it for your hay on a weight-for-weight basis.

Haylage does not keep well once the bag has been opened and should be used within five days in the winter, and two days in the summer. Re-wrap the unused portion to keep as much air away from it as possible.

Suitable substitutes
There are other ways of providing a fibre substitute for hay. For instance, well-soaked, unmolassed beet pulp goes a long way, is made up mainly of water so is not very fattening, and is enjoyed. As it has no molasses, it is unlikely to cause scouring, swells up a lot more than the molassed variety, and is eaten steadily, as it is not that exciting without molasses!

Also, consider topping up your younger pony with good - but not dusty - barley straw. The older pony will now be lacking muscle due to his age, so he might benefit from a higher protein content in his diet. The safe way to feed this is to use lucerne (or alfalfa, as it is known). A soaked mixture of lucerne nuts and unmolassed beet can be fed almost as a complete feed for elderly equines and they do very well on this.
Jane van Lennep

Vice squad

"WHAT CAUSES CRIB-BITING - AND HOW CAN IT BE STOPPED?"

Q We have a horse on our yard who cribs and the other livery clients do not want their horses stabled next to him. Could you tell me what causes this and if there is anything we can do to stop him?

A Surveys of stabled horses in the UK have indicated that over 15 per cent of domesticated horses exhibit 'stable vices', such as crib-biting and weaving. And many of these behaviours are considered an unsoundness, since they are thought to influence the horse's health and performance.

The term 'vice' implies that the fault lies with the horse, but the behaviour is more likely to be a symptom of the horse's attempt to cope with the unnatural environments in which he's placed for commercial purposes. Our modern-day breeds still seem to have certain in-built needs, and if they are released into semi-natural conditions, they will behave in ways very similar to their wild ancestors.

It is often the management system that is thought to be primarily responsible for causing these behaviour problems, and it is therefore both unfair and inaccurate to label these behaviours 'vices'. It's better to call them 'behavioural disorders' or, in some cases, 'stereotypies', the definition of which is a 'behaviour that is repeated with monotonous regularity and is fixed in all details'. Some researchers feel that these behaviours enable captive animals to cope with particular situations or environments. It may be that the animals' expectations are not being met by their surroundings, so they seek stimulation internally. If this is the case, then we can assume that horses exhibiting this behaviour have, or have had, problems in coping with their everyday environment.

The whys and wherefores

Stereotypic behaviour in horses is generally classified as either **locomotory** or **oral**:

● **Locomotory stereotypies** are often associated with confinement, restricted access to grazing and exercise areas, and a lack of environmental stimulation and social contact, leading to separation anxiety. Examples of locomotory stereotypies in the horse are: weaving (swinging the head and neck from side to side, sometimes including the whole body, and shifting the body weight from foreleg to foreleg) and box walking (pacing or circling around the stable).

● **Oral-based stereotypies** tend to be associated with feeding practices. Oral-based stereotypies include: wind-sucking (where the horse opens its mouth, contracts the pharyngeal musculature and appears to swallow or gulp air – although it is likely that the horse is actually only moving air into the mouth and pharynx); and crib-biting (which is the same as wind-sucking, but the horse also grabs a solid object with its teeth).

An inadequate diet plays a part in the development of oral stereotypies. The stabled performance horse is usually given a concentrated feed, but it has limited access to fibre. In its more natural state, the horse will spend up to 16 hours a day foraging. The stabled horse, in contrast, can eat all its nutritional requirements in two to three hours. Not only has the horse less bulk in its diet, but also more time to fill. It may be that oral-based activities alleviate some abdominal discomfort, due to the hightly concentrated diet and lack of fibre.

And recent studies have shown that oral stereotypies may develop because they lead to an increase in saliva production, which serves to neutralise acidity in the gut.

Prevention and cure

Once established, stereotypies are very difficult to correct. Treatments range from applying a collar to prevent the horse from cribbing or wind-sucking and anti-weaving bars on the stable door, to surgical procedures where the nerves, ligaments or muscles used in the behaviour are cut (neurectomy, myotomy). But the apparent solution of a behavioural disorder may lead to a welfare problem. If the performance of a behaviour helps alleviate frustration or stress, then preventing the horse from performing that behaviour could lead to further frustration.

Obviously, the best means of solving a problem is to prevent the behaviour from developing in the first place, and sometimes it can be reduced by changing a management system. For example, if a horse only performs the behaviour when it is isolated, the horse ideally needs to be with other horses. But if the problem behaviour has become 'fixed' (a habit) and emancipated (no longer associated with the initial cause), and is difficult to break, drug therapy may be advised – although little is yet known about this procedure.

An alternative and preferable approach to the problem is to prevent the behaviour from developing, by improving the quality of housing conditions through environmental enrichment – for example, by feeding. So try turning this horse out to graze for as long as possible. Or increase feeding time for stabled horses by providing the horse with more fibre (ad-lib hay).

Alternatively, to extend feeding time without increasing the amount of food, make the horse work harder for the same amount of food. For example, decrease the size of the holes in its haynet or feed it using a foraging device such as an Equiball. It delivers small food rewards, randomly in space and time, as the horse pushes it around the stable, and it may be used as a substitute for or in addition to the horse's usual rations.

I hope this helps with your problem – and good luck!
Natalie Waran

SUGGESTIONS AND THEORIES

Many horses may live in the same type of environment, but only some will develop abnormal behaviours. This might be due to an inherited predisposition to perform stereotypic behaviour, but there is a lack of scientific evidence to support this theory, due to the reluctance of owners to admit to the performance of such behaviours. And interestingly, it seems that 'warm-blooded' breeds are more likely to perform stereotypies than the cobs, native ponies and heavier breeds – possibly because they're more likely to be housed intensively.

It has also been suggested that weaning at an abnormally early age may encourage the development of stereotypies, especially oral types. It is thought that the abrupt end of the comforting suckling phase may be traumatic for some foals and it is replaced by other oral fixations when a horse is stressed in later life. It has been shown that 93.7 per cent of yearlings started exhibiting abnormal behaviours immediately following weaning.

Others believe that horses learn about these behaviours by mimicking others, but this has never been proven. In fact, experiments have shown that horses are not good at learning discrimination tasks by observing the behaviour of others. So the truth might be simply that horses on the same yard are exposed to similar stresses and are, therefore, just as likely to develop a behavioural problem.

Can I make a claim?

"IS IT AN OFFENCE TO RIDE ON A FOOTPATH?"

Q I ride my horse to and from work daily, but had an accident while riding on a path which I thought was a public right of way – having seen other riders and cyclists using it. My horse stepped in a puddle which turned out to be 45cms deep and cut her leg on some glass. She had to be stabled for three-and-a-half months and she has still not fully healed. I tried claiming expenses from the County Council, but have been told it is an offence to ride on a footpath. What can I do now?

A As a general rule, if you enter on to somebody else's land and are injured by a hazard of which the owner was aware or ought to have been aware, then you will have a right of action against the landowner. This may apply even if you are a trespasser.

Whether liability arises in each particular case depends on various circumstances, such as the direct cause of the accident, the extent of the owner's knowledge of the risk presented by the hazard, the degree of risk and the steps that the owner could have taken to have reduced this, the extent of the injury and the likelihood that you would be on his land either as a guest or as a trespasser.

A complicated business

The situation concerning injury sustained on pubic paths and roads is complicated by the complexity of the law relating to public rights of way, and it is not possible to deal with these here in any depth. But if a public bridleway or footpath is registered as such by the local authority in the Definitive Map, then the surface of such a path or bridleway vests in the local highway authority, whose responsibility it is to maintain the surface.

This does not mean the local authority must maintain it to the same standard as a public road. The duty is to maintain the surface to a standard sufficient to allow safe passage for those entitled to use it. In the case of a footpath or bridleway, the existence of deep potholes that would be undetectable when filled with rainwater would probably make the local authority liable, should a walker or rider be injured by falling into such a pothole.

In the circumstances outlined in your letter, the extent of the local authority's liability is difficult to determine. Your case is unusual in that you rode the route regularly as a means of getting to and from work, as opposed simply to recreational use. However if, as seems likely, the local authority is liable, then your losses flowing directly from the accident should be recoverable, including the cost of treatment of the injury and additional costs of care and keep. The cost of an alternative means of transport to work may also be recoverable, if you can show that this is genuinely an additional cost.

The difficulties

Two factors, however, pose some difficulty when bringing the claim. The first of these is that you appear to have ridden the path in question on a daily basis, and the council may be able to successfully establish that you knew the route well and should have been aware of the existence of the potholes – and accordingly should have been able to avoid them. This is termed 'contributory negligence' and may serve to reduce the proportion of damages that you would otherwise be able to recover.

The second difficulty is that you appear to have had the benefit of insurance which has covered at least a part of your losses. If the insurance company has paid out on a claim made by you, they will effectively have taken an assignment of your right of action against the local authority to the extent of the amount paid out under their policy.

Unless you refund to the insurance company any such monies, it will be for the insurance company to decide whether or not they wish to pursue the claim against the council. This means that you will only be entitled to claim against the council your uninsured losses, namely the expenses to which you have been put which have not been met by the insurance company.

In conclusion . . .

It is not a criminal offence to ride a horse on a public footpath, although it may be trespass as against the owner of the underlying land. Even if the path in question was a public footpath as opposed to a public bridleway, the fact that you and others appear to have ridden your horses along it regularly, tends to indicate that the local authority should have been aware of such use and of the risk of injury from concealed potholes.

Richard Chamberlain

Herd instincts

"MY HORSE OVERTAKES OTHER HORSES BEFORE COMING TO A STANDSTILL."

Q I have a problem with my rather clever and sensitive 11-year-old Russian Budyonny. If we canter and there is a horse behind us, he will not go forward until the other horse has caught up. If we canter with only horses in front, he does all he can to overtake them, barges to the front and then comes to a virtual standstill. If hacked out alone he is quite sharp. Budyonnys are raced in Russia - could this be the reason for his strange behaviour? Or could it be a result of him being 'cut' late, as is the custom in Russia?

A I think it is unlikely that your horse's difficulties are a result of having been a racehorse. More likely, he was taken out of training because of his bad behaviour - as he is, he would be a nightmare on the racecourse.

However, if he was cut late this is a more plausible trigger for his current behaviour. He is obviously very insecure, needing other horses in close proximity.

As an entire, he would have been denied the company of other horses from an early age, when most young horses are learning how to

respond to others and how they in turn respond to the youngster. Your horse's behaviour is not untypical of late-cut geldings.

Equine etiquette

The solution is not easy. Having missed out on his early learning or normal equine etiquette, he really needs to be left to sort out his problems under the guidance of other horses! Sadly, this involves a degree of kicking and biting until the 'problem' child learns how to act sensibly and so is able to build a level of security and self confidence.

He will inflict as well as risk receiving injury, and it is hard to imagine how any other horse owners would be persuaded to be party to such a scenario. It is usually less traumatic with single sex groups. If you can find anywhere for him to be turned out on a regular basis with at least three or four other horses, the benefits to your boy would eventually be immeasurable.

Schooling solutions

The only other way to tackle the problem is through schooling. It may sound too obvious, but a well-trained and disciplined horse will learn to accept the authority of his rider and will certainly feel better for it.

Go right back to basics if you have to, teaching him to stand, walk, turn, change gait, whatever you ask of him, in a safe area and with or without the close proximity of other horses. Treat him like the stallion he probably feels he is. Whips and spurs are not the answer, although it is advisable to carry a whip at all times when riding an entire.

It will be much easier to sort out his misdemeanours in the schooling area than out hacking. If he grinds to a halt for example and refuses to budge, you can sit it out if you have to. He does not sound like the sort of horse who would want to stand still for long. Be strong when he is bad and reward him when he makes the right moves. Never lose your temper as patience and firmness are much stronger devices in the long term, for a sustained good result.

Developing a partnership

Avoid situations where you know you will be in trouble. Repeating bad behaviour will reinforce it and battles are remembered for longer than their outcome. Build on what you know you can do well so that you work towards developing a partnership whereby he respects you and trusts you and wants to please you. It is important that you get the right result whatever you ask of him and avoid those frustrating situations where neither of you are happy.

It can help to talk to other people with similar problems. Try to make contact with someone who has a stallion in ridden work, of any breed, to have a chat about how they cope in company. Your horse's apparent nervousness could well be the key to his improvement as he is possibly very anxious to please.

Remember the old adage - you tell a gelding what to do, ask a mare and discuss things with a stallion. Keep explaining, listen to his arguments and show him that your way is best.
Fliss Gillott

Understanding COPD

"WHAT IS THE BEST WAY TO TREAT COPD?"

Q My mare developed a cough last year which was treated with antibiotics. Her cough has recurred twice since then and it now looks as though she has COPD. What is the best way to treat the condition, and how can I prevent further attacks?

A COPD - or Recurrent Airway Obstruction - is probably the commonest cause of chronic coughing in the horse. It is caused by a hypersensitivity in the lining of the lung air tubes to fungal spores and dust. Its most similar equivalent condition in man is asthma.

It is not uncommon for a horse which has never previously coughed, suddenly to become sensitised to stable dusts, and this often seems to follow a primary viral infection. This may well be what happened in your own horse's case, and her first episode of respiratory disease and coughing could well have been due to infection.

In some horses it seems that once the respiratory tract has become sensitised, it remains sensitised for a period of time, sometimes the remainder of the horse's life. To be sure that your horse is suffering from COPD, we would probably need to have more information about the horse. Firstly, does the cough disappear when the horse is turned out in the summer? Most horses with COPD improve considerably when not exposed to a dusty stable environment.

Secondly, does your horse improve clinically and does the cough rate reduce when medicated with clenbuterol (Ventipulmin) only?

This is a fairly sensitive indicator that broncho-spasm and mucus accumulation are the cause of your horse's cough, in that clenbuterol only acts by relaxing the airways and is not aimed at infection of other causes of coughing.

If the answer to both of these is positive, then it is likely that your horse is suffering from COPD. Once you have established this for sure, then you can go on to design a programme to minimise your horse's exposure to the allergens which cause the problem.

Managing COPD

Your horse should be bedded on newspaper or shavings and these should be kept clean and not allowed to rot in the stable. The hay should be fully immersed in water for one minute prior to feeding. Longer immersion than this 'leaches' a lot of the goodness out of the hay and is not to be recommended. All hay should be fed on the floor, so that the horse is not standing at a haynet pulling clouds of dust particles into the air which he subsequently breathes in.

Your stable should be well ventilated at all times. If this means leaving the top door open and having a window at the back, then so be it. If you are worried about the cold, you can always put more rugs on the horse and standing bandages on all four legs to keep your horse warm enough. Remember that horses were designed to live in fields and were never designed to cope with the air quality which results from putting them in buildings.

Treating the symptoms

If you do all of the above and your horse is still plagued with COPD symptoms, then you could consider medicating your horse with a drug designed to prevent the allergic response from taking place.

Unlike Ventipulmin, these drugs are not designed to relieve the symptoms of COPD, but to block the cause. One such drug is sodium cromoglycate. This used to be available as a drug called Cromovet which was administered as an aerosol by a face mask. Unfortunately, along with many other medications, this has now lost its product licence. However, it is legal for your veterinary surgeon to prescribe the nearest licensed human equivalent and, fortunately, there is such a preparation made primarily for use in treating hay fever in man as an eyedrop.

This can be administered by nebuliser in exactly the same way as Cromovet used to be. The drug company concerned, Schering-Plough, would be happy to advise on the use of this product if your veterinary surgeon were to contact them. There are also now available face masks for horses which will fit the common 'puffer' inhalers used to control asthma in man. Bronchodilators, which open up the airways, corticosteroids, which suppress inflammation, and the drug mentioned above which prevents the allergic response taking place, are all available in this form, and their use is often very effective when given this way.

Although you do not prevent your horse inhaling dust, you do put a stop to the abnormal allergic reaction which is triggering your horse's symptoms.

Rob Pilsworth

Building a manège

"I WANT TO BUILD MY OWN MANÈGE."

Q Could you give me any advice on building an outdoor manège, and are there any books on the subject which might help?

A There are many firms which supply surfaces for outdoor manèges, and these advertise in the equestrian press. Most of these will supply for self-build projects and I am sure will be happy to advise. Choose a large company with nationwide experience, or a well-established local company that has knowledge of local conditions. There is an enormous choice.

It can be a good idea to find out what has worked well for someone else who has built a manège in your area, and chat to them about how it was constructed, and what differences they would make if they were to do it all again.

The more you can read up on the subject, the better. J A Allen, the equestrian publishers, have a book which could help: *All-Weather Surfaces for Horses* by Ray Lodge and Susan Shanks. It has recently been revised and enlarged, so should be up-to-date. Any good bookshop should be able to get it for you.

Whatever your research proves is the best option for you, where you can, use local materials, as haulage is so expensive. Remember that natural, biological surfaces, such as wood bark for instance, have a natural tendency to rot, so will not be as lasting as mineral-based surfaces. Some surfaces need more maintenance than others, but tend to be cheaper. You will need to look carefully at drainage and how the surface performs when wet if you are in a high rainfall area.

Jane van Lennep

Lengthy lameness

"HE'S STILL LAME."

Q I have a pony who received a kick three years ago. This resulted in a lameness in the near hindleg after about three months. Four different vets have examined him, none of whom seem to be able to find the cause of his lameness. He is on one sachet of bute a day and seems quite happy in himself, but I do not know where to go from here.

A The following need to be clarified before making any suggestions:
● Is the pony actually sound on one sachet of bute or is this a mechanical lameness?
● How severe is the lameness now? Does it affect one or more gaits?
● What form have the previous diagnoses taken? Has scintigraphy (bone scanning) or thermal imaging been used? Has anybody looked into the stifle joint or assessed the nervous supply to the hind leg?
● Has all the muscle returned, or is there still partial muscle wastage?

The body adjusts

After a severe injury, although muscles recover, the affected limb will always be weaker than the healthy side. The is because the body adjusts its balance and movement during the recovery period, but forgets to 'reset' the programme once the injury has healed. The result is a mechanical deficit, rather than a painful problem.

Nowadays, diagnostic techniques are so sophisticated that it should be possible to identify the exact cause of lamenss. However, none of us have X-ray vision, so that for anything more than educated guesswork, you do have to go to a referral centre - for example, Rossdale & Partners in Newmarket, Suffolk, or Liphook Equine Veterinary Hospital in Hampshire.

The possibilities suggested by your description of the injury are the presence of a small fragment of bone, and injury to a nerve (the sciatic nerve can easily be traumatised) or an injury to a muscle, such as the semitendinosus.

It is also possible that the cause of the lameness is now no longer in the hind limb itself. Jarring to one leg is capable of throwing the whole body out of balance and if the pony had to move suddenly, it is quite possible that the bones in the neck are locked awkwardly, making it impossible for the pony to return to soundness.

Sara Wyche

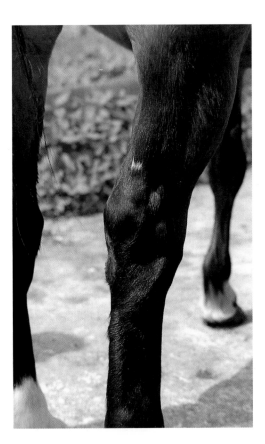

Crisis of confidence

"I'VE LOST MY CONFIDENCE AND I DON'T KNOW WHY!"

Q I seem to have lost my condidence on my eight-year-old pony, but am not sure why! Generally, she's fairly sensible, but when we go uphill, she has a habit of rushing. I've changed her bit from a snaffle to a Kimblewick as I needed a more efficient braking system on corners and in trot. I'm at college and don't ride as often as I'd like, but am determined to get back into the saddle, ride confidently on my own again and compete.

A It sounds as though there has not been any particular reason for you to lose confidence, other than you not being able to ride regularly and that your mare can be strong at times. Once you have more opportunities to get back into the saddle part of the problem will resolve itself.

Feeling in control

The question of feeling in control, however, could take a little longer to sort out. Let's try to summerise exactly what the problems are - rushing up hills, rushing in trot and through corners, not respecting a snaffle bit. I think you were wise to switch to a Kimblewick rather than battle with the snaffle and bruise her mouth, so now you just need to learn how to use this extra control effectively and sympathetically to deal with the rushing.

Lines of communication

With any horse or pony displaying a tendency to rush and therefore lose balance, it is important for the rider to learn how to establish a steady rhythm, whichever gait you are riding in. As ever, this is best practised in walk - up hills, down hills, turning, circling - always in a regular, active but unhurried stride.

At any sign of rushing, slow down just a fraction beyond where you want to be, so that you have a chance to take the pressure off and lighten the contact. This gives you thinking time if the pony starts speeding again, to gently hold as the correct rhythm is reached.

This can be repeated as often as is necessary, not leaving the reins loose and flapping, but with just enough contact to keep all lines of communication open.

A light feel on the mouth

Hanging on to the front end will encourage the pony to argue and fight to get the reins back. This is not in the least surprising as it must be very uncomfortable to have strong and unremitting pressure on the bars of your mouth. Your job is to teach your pony that staying in a steady pace ensures a light feel on the mouth and makes all the work easier for you both. When you get a good result, tell your mare she is a good girl. If you can do this in walk, then, and only then, try the same routine in trot and around turns.

Three steps to relaxation

Staying 'relaxed' (not collapsed!) yourself is not easy. As a rider, you should be calm but alert, active but as still as possible and beautifully balanced at all times. There are ways to make this less of an uphill task.

1. Relax your seat. The first thing to work on is the lower part of your back and your seat muscles. If you overtighten your seat muscles, especially when you are anxious and not because you are consciously 'using' your seat, you will almost certainly also tighten your lower back. This sets you against the movement of the horse's back which will encourage the horse to rush and become tense as well.

An easy correction is to 'soften' your seat which in turn will free your back muscles and allow you to follow the movement naturally.

2. Loosen your shoulders. A tense rider will hunch their shoulders which in turn leads to stiff arms and hands, and a horse which displays all the signs of being uncomfortable in its mouth and heavy or strong against the rider's hands.

3. Breathe properly. If you are tensing your seat, back and shoulders, you are certainly not breathing properly and at the same time, pulling your stomach in. This is a classic defensive posture which does not lead to good riding!

Try to breathe using all your lungs - not just the top of them. Doing this will also help to sort out the postural problems I've already mentioned, or at least make it much easier to do so. Breathe as slowly as you can, focusing as much on breathing all the way out as all the way in.

If you remember nothing else when your head is full of trying to keep a rhythm, release the contact and sit up straight, at least take a deep breath and really blow it all the way out again, just the once to start with.

If you cannot cope with thinking about your breathing, talking or singing is better than nothing. Silent and shallow breathing is a recipe for building tension and I am sure if you can work on your tension, it will reap massive dividends with dealing with your pony's tension and rushing.
Fliss Gillott

Buying a horse

"THEY LIED ABOUT MY HORSE'S AGE!"

Q **I recently bought a horse which I had vetted prior to purchase. I had one or two problems with him not gaining weight and I decided to have his teeth checked. I was amazed when the dentist told me the horse was 23 and not 12, as I had been told by the vendor. The original vet had confirmed his age as 12 at the vetting.**

A This letter raises two distinct and separate issues. The first is whether or not a claim can successfully be brought against the vendor of the horse in respect of the incorrect description, and the second is whether or not a claim can be successfully brought against the vet.

Sale of Goods Act
If the vendor was a dealer, then the Sale of Goods Act 1979 will apply. The horse would have to be of satisfactory quality, taking into account age and fitness for the purposes for which it was being sold.

Notwithstanding the fact that you had the

horse vetted, if the vendor was a dealer, there has been a clear breach of contract and you will be entitled to return the horse and to demand a refund.

Alternatively, if you wish to keep the horse, you may be entitled to do so and claim damages for the difference in value between what you thought you were buying and what you actually bought.

Misrepresentation

If the vendor was a private individual, the Sale of Goods Act will not apply. However, even a private vendor must not make misrepresentations of fact. If a vendor makes untrue or misleading representations and the purchaser relies upon those representations, then the vendor may be liable to pay damages and the purchaser may be entitled to demand a refund.

However, you would need to prove that you must have relied upon the representation made by the vendor when purchasing the horse. This may be in doubt simply because you had the horse vetted.

A breach of contract

One other possible ground of claim exists, and this depends upon whether or not the age of the horse was 'a term' of the contract. If you made it clear that what you wanted was a 12-year-old horse and the vendor assured you that this was a 12-year-old horse, then the horse's age may have been a term of the contract. However, in legal terms, this would be difficult to establish.

The horse was not being sold purely by its description as a 12-year-old, but by personal inspection and veterinary examination. It is also possible that the vendor may have had no idea of the horse's true age.

A claim against the vet

This leaves the question of a possible claim against the vet based on negligence. In order to succeed, you would have to show that the vet owed you a duty of care, that he had broken that duty in his examination and report of the horse and that you had suffered a loss as a result of the breach of duty, which was reasonably foreseeable.

There can be no doubt that the vet owed you a duty of care, but it is much more difficult to determine whether or not the vet has broken that duty in his assessment of the horse's age. 'Ageing' a horse by physical examination is not an exact science. However, It is clear in this case that the vet seriously misjudged the horse's age. Whether or not that misjudgement amounts to professional negligence depends upon the prevailing body of expert opinion within the veterinary profession.

If you are to successfully pursue a claim, it will be necessary to obtain an expert opinion from at least one equine specialist vet, as to the degree of accuracy that a reasonably competent equine vet should display when assessing a horse's age.

If you are able to successfully bring a claim, you will be able to recover damages. The level of such damages may be the cost of a suitable replacement horse. Unfortunately, the law requires that any claimant must 'mitigate his or her loss', which means that you must take all reasonable steps to reduce the amount of your loss and, therefore, your claim. You would probably be required to sell the horse for as much as you could obtain, or, to give credit for the true value of the horse by way of a deduction from the damages.

I have every sympathy for you in that you appear to have done everything correctly when setting out to buy a horse, only to have ended up with one that is of little use to you. This situation is made more difficult if the value of your claim is below the current County Court limit of £5,000. Claims for less than £5,000 are usually dealt with under the Small Claims procedure under which solicitors' costs are not usually recoverable even by the successful claimant. The fees of expert witnesses should be recoverable, but to bring a claim of this nature without a solicitor would be a daunting task for most people.

Richard Chamberlain

Kicking the habit

"HOW CAN I DEAL WITH A HORSE WHO KICKS?"

Q **I have a 12-year-old Thoroughbred former point-to-pointer who kicks. He has a lovely nature and is a very enjoyable ride. However, in company I have to put a red ribbon on his tail to warn others, although he never tries to kick his stablemate.**

A A confirmed kicker is unlikely to mend his ways, although it helps to deal with the situation if you are able to glean some idea of what is going on in the horse's mind.

Why do horses kick?
Kicking is generally a sign of insecurity rather than naked aggression, which would tie in with the fact that the horse you mention does not kick the horse with which he is already familiar.

A horse's insecurity will not always be manifested by nervous behaviour. It may be that he is unsure of his status with other horses - that is, if you like, where he stands in the pecking order. Rather like people who feel they need to exaggerate their own merit when talking to others by putting down other people, for example, or boasting, some horses will display antisocial behaviour if they are forced into close proximity with horses they do not know.

Mares are more likely to kick to defend their 'honour', to repel any possible, untimely attempts at an amorous advance. In this sense, kicking is a form of self defence, although there may be a strong element of territorialism involved as well. A gelding has no more status in a herd than a weak colt, and may be aware that he is challenged in being able to stand his ground.

Encouraging good behaviour
The fact that your horse is a kicker does not mean that he is wicked or has a bad temperament. Perhaps if he had more time at liberty with a number of other horses, he may begin to understand that an unknown horse may not, in fact, be about to drive him away.

Living with a 'herd' is the best way for a horse to develop an understanding of how other horses behave, and when there is no cause for concern. The trouble that a great many Thoroughbreds have is they have not had this opportunity early in life, so it may take a long time for them to establish what should have been learnt as part of being a horse.

If you can turn him out with others, this would be the best thing for him, especially if there are a number of changes within the group over time.

A word of caution - hind shoes are a serious hazard under these circumstances, as a kick from a shod horse can be ultimately fatal or at least cause serious injury. Perhaps your horse could have his hind shoes taken off and be turned out to grass when he is in light work.

In the meantime, stick to the red ribbon and play safe. Remember, your horse cannot kick without stopping first, and be firm with your riding, keeping him well between hand and leg all the time. Tell him off if he does throw a leg and try to overcome his insecurities through discipline and obedience coupled with reassurance.

Whatever the excuse, kicking is a dangerous disobedience which can be schooled out with the correct, strong approach. Even so, a kicker is always potentially a kicker and should always be treated with care.

Fliss Gillott

A question of trust

"I DON'T TRUST MY OWN HORSE."

Q My four-year-old cob is very sweet, but I don't trust him. He knows he can get me off if he bucks and he's getting very boisterous – particularly when I go into his field. As he lives in a field by himself – the yard owner doesn't like keeping a lot of horses together – he starts to play with me as if I'm another horse and it hurts! He has also started biting people. What should I do?

A There is nothing worse than not trusting your own horse. The whole enjoyment of owning a horse involves the bond that you and the horse form, and the fun you can have together.

Your horse seems to view you as a playmate and, unfortunately, sees you as lower in the social hierarchy! Any youngster will test the limits, and all young horses need firm, consistent and informed handling and training, so that they learn appropriate behaviour.

Your horse is not only testing the limits, he is also in need of a structured training programme. As a four-year-old in his natural environment (ie, if he were a feral horse), he'd be taught 'good manners' or proper social behaviour by the older mares in the group. And he would spend a lot of time play-fighting with other young males. What he is doing is not, therefore, unnatural – just unwanted!

You need help!

You need to seek expert help with your cob. He needs to learn that you are not prepared to be his playmate, and that biting and charging are all unacceptable – but that being nice to handle and behaving well under saddle will all be rewarded. You have to replace his games with your games!

Also, speak with the yard owner, to see if they'd be more flexible with their field routine. Horses need to interact freely, and keeping them in separate fields where they have little contact is, in my opinion, inhumane. Being such social creatures means that they crave companions, and depriving them of normal social contact will often lead to the sort of behaviour problem that your horse has developed.

I suggest that you put him in a field with a couple of older and wiser mares, and supervise the interactions – I am sure that he will learn to socialise with his own kind.

Natalie Waran

Living with laminitis

"CAN YOU SUGGEST A WAY OF PUTTING CONDITION ON MY HORSE WHO SUFFERS FROM LAMINITIS?"

Q **I own a 17hh eight-year-old gelding who is prone to laminitis. He developed it last August and has now made a full recovery. My vet has advised that I can bring him back into work again, but I'm worried as he is in poor condition at the moment. What's the best way to put condition on him without risking another attack?**

A Dealing with a horse who is prone to laminitis – and in full work – should present relatively few difficulties, as long as certain rules are observed.

What causes laminitis?
Laminitis is a direct result of fermentation of excessive carbohydrates in the large bowel of the horse. This appears to produce toxins which circulate in the bloodstream and exert their effects at a distance on the blood vessels.

The only blood vessels where the effect of these toxins is important seem to be those in the distal limb and foot. And it is these changes that lead to the degeneration of the laminae, and the subsequent pain and problems. It is therefore carbohydrate intake that you have to most closely monitor and watch.

Healthy condition
It's ideal that your horse is in relatively lean condition and he should remain so if he is to stay free of laminitis. This does not mean that

he should be thin. Nor does it mean that you won't be able to feed him adequately for exercise.

Most people avoid the use of bran in laminitics on account of its high phosphorous content. Think about feeding some or all of the horse's hay requirement as alfalfa hay. This is high in protein and excellent in biological value. It is also a digestible fibre and, therefore, much less likely to contribute to laminitis. It has been shown experimentally that a horse can live on alfalfa hay as its entire source of nutrition and maintain good body weight.

Obviously, if the horse is working, then extra calories will be required, so consider using one of the high-fat supplements. This is a way of getting energy into the horse without the carbohydrates. Similarly, a high fibre chaff-based feed could be used if further nutrition is required.

Working out a ration

The best advice really is to decide what feeding regime you wish to pursue and then have the actual feed components checked by a nutritionist. When you've decided on your feeds, measure the daily feed your horse will actually get in terms of bowls and jugs into some polythene bags. Then weigh the constituents accurately before formulating your proposed ration sheet.

Most of the reputable feed companies will employ or have access to a nutritionist with a computer programme into which your feed can be typed to check that the levels are correct. There may be a small fee for this, but it will certainly be less than the cost of dealing with laminitis in the future.

Risk times

With regard to grazing, it's interesting that your horse developed laminitis first in August. Most people's perception of the risk period for laminitis is during the growth of spring grass. Unfortunately, there is a second risk period at the end of the summer, which most people forget about.

The reason for this is that rapidly growing grass, supplied with abundant nutrients, has a high carbohydrate content in terms of sugars in the grass itself. These conditions occur in spring

PREVENTING FURTHER ATTACKS

■ **Avoid access to grazing for more than half an hour during spring and autumn.**
■ **Find a small paddock that the horse can graze down to the ground and use this during these high-risk times.**
■ **During the whole mid-summer period and the entire winter, the horse could probably be left out without serious risk, but a careful watch should be kept on his bodily condition to make sure that he is not getting fat.**

because of the lack of growth of any grass during the winter, allowing micronutrients in the soil to build up.

When the day lengthens and the ground temperature rises, the grass suddenly begins to grow and has abundant nutrients. During the summer, the feed quality of the grass diminishes considerably because of drought and lack of available nutrients. At the end of a long dry period, the coming of autumn rains releases nutrients once again to the roots and a second flush of grass occurs at this time. This can often be as dangerous, if not more so, than that which occurs in spring.
Rob Pilsworth

Matching horse and rider

"WHAT WEIGHT CAN A HORSE CARRY?"

Q Is there a simple formula to work out the maximum weight of rider that a horse can carry?

A There is no cut and dried answer to this as there are so many variables to take into account. In the end, it is down to the individual to make an informed decision faced with the horse, the rider in question and the particular circumstances prevailing at the time.

Pound for pound
I am always sceptical about basing a weight for the rider on the weight of the horse. This may work on a fit horse in ideal condition, but can hardly be appropriate for a fat and unfit horse whose back and limbs may already be under strain from the horse's own excess weight.

The formula of one sixth of the horse's bodyweight to give the maximum rider weight would start to look like a penalty for overindulging on the horse's part. If there was a method for gauging the horse's muscle tone and relating that to size and weight, the result would be more meaningful.

The rider's conformation
We need to take into account not only fitness, but also the rider's experience and skill. Then there is weight distribution. A leggy rider is an easier burden than a short-legged rider, especially if the short-legged rider is broad shouldered and has poor balance. The lower the rider's centre of balance, the less strain is put on the horse's back should the rider not remain directly over the horse's centre of balance.

An unfit rider is more likely to lose balance than a fit rider, either through tiredness or lack of strength and, therefore, control.

Carrying too much weight?
- the signs to look out for
Ultimately, the horse will tell you if he has too much weight on his back. The signs to look out for are:
● excessive sweating;
● a tendency to stumble;
● shortening of stride;
● dropping the back - this may happen when the

rider first mounts up;
● a reluctance to go forward as well as usual;
● napping and refusing to work at all, when this is out of character;
● tenderness in the back area after work, possibly for a number of days afterwards.

These signs may seem extreme, but even slight changes will indicate that the horse is not happy. Where there is serious doubt as to whether or not a horse should carry a particular rider, it is wise to seek professional advice and to take it. An experienced instructor, an equitherapist, a vet, or even a fully qualified saddler are all people who should have a feel for what is right and will be prepared to give an honest opinion based on what they see in front of them.
Fliss Gillott

Change of character

"COULD MY MARE'S CHANGE OF CHARACTER BE HORMONAL?"

Q **I bought my 15hh, eight-year-old cob mare seven months ago. When I moved her to her new yard I removed her hind shoes to turn her out. Everything was fine at first. Then, after two weeks, she became reluctant to move and didn't want to go out. I was told she had sore feet, so I put her shoes back on.**

She improved for about a week but suddenly, out of the blue she started bucking, walking sideways and refusing to go forwards. This happened three or four times, so I got her back and saddle checked - both were fine. I am at a loss as to what has caused this change in her behaviour. Could it be hormonal?

A Your mare's behaviour is certainly very unusual. If this started when she came in season, then it would be reasonable to expect an improvement when she went off, even if the improvement only lasted for a few days. A lot of mares do start ovulating in January or February, or at least showing strong signs of oestrus, so the timing of this mare's change in attitude could tie in with this. It may be worth keeping a note of any pattern, or possible pattern, in her behaviour developing over a period of time, just in case there is a link.

Eliminating allergies

Have you changed her diet at all? You could try cutting her feed back to the very basic constituents, to see if there is any possible reacton to a particular foodstuff.

This would mean avoiding all compound feeds for the time being, as they contain a number of different constituents, making it difficult for you to pinpoint any particular reaction. Be drastic and cut out everything except hay, grass and carrots or apples in small quantities. Do this for a week and see if there is any improvement. If not, then the chances are that her behaviour is not dietary based. If there is an improvement, then start adding other feedstuffs one at a time, only as you feel she needs them.

It is possible that she is slightly colicky all the time, so make sure she is being regularly wormed, and that the worming is successful. It may be a good idea to talk to your vet about this aspect of things, and maybe ask for his suggestions as to a possible cause of her erraticism.

Time for turn-out

Since you had her hind shoes put back on, is she still able to be turned out with other horses as often as before? Cobs do generally enjoy being out as often as possible, so if her time at grass, when she is able to exercise and socialise, is limited, then she may simply need more playtime. Try to observe her behaviour with other horses and see if she is as vile to all living creatures as she is to you!

Getting tough

If, after all this, you are no nearer to finding a cause for her malaise, then you are going to have to toughen up and sort her out. For this you will almost certainly need the help of someone more experienced than yourself, though ultimately she will need to learn that you are the boss, that your word is law, and that this is the only way for the two of you to become friends again.

She must be reprimanded for any bad behaviour towards you. Your reactions must be quick and decisive, sufficient to startle her out of her bad mood, or whatever it is that is unsettling her.

Any sign of improvement should be rewarded with a kind word and a pat if you are close to her, but I would advise against any form of titbit feeding if she is handy with her teeth. Don't waste time petting her, but rather do what you have to do efficiently and with minimum fuss.

Keep your lessons short and to the point, even if all you have done is to walk once round the paddock under saddle. Be consistent with all your handling of her. She must respect your personal space and be obedient to your commands.

A change of scene

It may be significant that her behaviour deteriorated so soon after moving yard. There could be any number of reasons for this. Perhaps the daily routine is less well organised, or perhaps she is being bullied by the other horses and is suffering an equine form of depression.

Don't give up, though, as there is a solution out there somewhere! As long as there really is no physical problem, I'm sure you will find the answer.
Fliss Gillott

Tricky customer

"MY HORSE KNOWS I'M AFRAID OF HIM."

Q **My daughter owns a three-year-old gelded half Thoroughbred, one quarter Dutch warmblood, one quarter Arab. The problem is he knows I am afraid of him, playing up when I handle him. Recently, he bit me on my arm and caused bruising.**

He is about 15.3hh and is very sturdy. He has been trained by a professional trainer who didn't have difficulty with him. He's very mouthy, and he cribs as well. He gets a very mischievous look on his face and I know I am 'in for it'. What can I do to gain his respect, or is it too late?

A It is not too late to gain this horse's respect. At only three years old, he is still very susceptible to learning and should be given plenty to think about and occupy his mind. Although he is a gelding, it would seem that he has retained some of his coltish characteristics. He has reached the age when his instincts are telling him to assert himself as a male, hence the mouthiness.

Your horse sees you as a weaker member of the 'herd', which is why his behaviour is worse towards you than to your professional trainer.

The trouble with having home-bred youngsters that are rather special, is that they often get a little spoilt when they are young! Spoiling is no longer on the agenda with this horse until he has learned to behave like a gentleman.

Teaching good behaviour
Always put a headcollar on him and tie him up whenever you go into the stable, so that he is unable to reach and bite. Teach him in no uncertain terms to move over or back on command, and to stay out of your way. Carry a short stick, if you have to, and use it on his chest to reinforce your voice commands. If you are not very tough with him, he could end up causing someone serious damage.

Avoid spending more time with him than is necessary to do what is needed. If you hang around just for the sake of it, he will start treating you as a playmate, an equal, or someone to dominate. Absolutely never feed him tit-bits, even when he is being a good boy, as this encourages mouthiness. Pat him and praise him with your voice when he is good and he will know you are pleased.

Protective gear
To aid your confidence, and to protect yourself as far as possible against serious injury, make sure you are properly protected when you handle your boy. Wear long sleeves, gloves and a hard hat as well as strong boots. He is obviously capable of controlling himself and behaving well, so there is no reason to suppose that he will not learn to behave for you.
Fliss Gillott

Conquering equine nerves

"MY HORSE IS AFRAID OF EVERYTHING - HELP!"

Q I live on a farm with lots of machinery, and have a horse who seems to be afraid of everything - even a dog running in front of her! She jumps and then gallops off, with me on her back. Please help!

A Your horse seems to have become extremely sensitised to many of the sudden and loud stimuli that surround her on the farm.

The extreme response of running away is the normal reaction of a frightened horse that is trying to remove itself from what it sees as a potentially life-threatening situation! However, each time she runs away, she is reinforcing her fear and, in addition, she is learning that she is stronger than you, and that she can ignore your aids to stop.

It is possible to retrain her, but you will need to try to ensure that during the first initial stages of her retraining, you have someone strong and experienced to help. You will be able to carry out most of the stable-based desensitisation yourself, but when you move onto linking the sound with the presence of a tractor or car, then you will need to make sure that you are properly in control.

Firstly, I suggest that you consult with your vet to ensure that your horse's eyes, and especially her ears, are functioning normally, so that you can rule out any clinical possibilities of a behaviour problem.

Once you are convinced that your horse is physically fine, then you could try a desensitisation programme, combined with a management plan, to see if her behaviour response to environmental distrubances can be reduced.

Management tips

Test whether you can reduce your horse's response to loud noise by padding her ears with home-made ear muffs. You may be able to do this when you know that loud noises will be a problem eg when riding in traffic, when she is

47

being transported, etc.

Ensure that the people driving tractors around the farm reduce their speed and the engine noise where possible; you don't want to have her frightened unnecessarily.

Also, see if there is an older, calmer companion for her to hack out with, so that she can learn from his/her behaviour.

How to desensitise the horse

Make a continuous recording of car and tractor sounds and play it to her, whilst in the stable, initially at low volume, and reward her relaxed response with carrots. Slowly build up the volume and the 'abruptness' of starting the tape over a few days, only progressing on to the next stage once she has shown you she is relaxed (ie not responding, and eating her carrots). Don't worry if you have to go back a stage occasionally. Just be consistent and calm. Change the tape recordings so that she gets familiar with children noises, dog noises etc.

Once you are happy that she is no longer concerned with the sounds, start to link them with staged 'settings', such as cars moving slowly (combining sight and sound), then faster, then do the same with tractors and children. This is where you will need people to help you, and ensure you can keep control of your mare.

Introduce each new setting in stages, and build up from being on the ground with your horse, to in the saddle. Make sure everything is under your control, so that your horse is never worried and is always rewarded for her calm response. Eventually she should no longer respond to stimuli which once worried her.

Calming words

You could also try to link her calm, relaxed state with a certain word signal. For example, she could be trained to associate the words 'be calm' said in a certain way, with carrots and a relaxed situation, then you can use this word signal in situations that she normally finds frightening, such as when she is hacking around the farm.

Be methodical

I suggest that you keep a diary so that you can monitor what you have achieved with your mare. Also, carry out a session each day, giving only carrots or whatever you choose as her reward, during a desensitisation session.

Be persistent. If a horse has been deprived of experiences she should have had when younger, then it will take time and patience to build up her confidence. I am sure that, given time, your horse will learn to cope with the challenges of living with the machines in her environment.

However, if she continues to show a fear response to noises, dogs, etc, despite your efforts, then you may need to consider whether she might be happier living in a quieter environment.

Natalie Waran

Trespassers beware!

"CAN YOU DEFINE MY LEGAL RESPONSIBILITY?"

Q **My horses have been eating some hedging on my neighbour's boundary fence. Is it my responsibility legally to prevent them from doing this and pay for any damage, or is it up to my neighbour? I would also like to know if my horses qualify as 'agricultural livestock' as my neighbour is concerned over this issue.**

A This is an interesting problem. Dealing first with the classification of horses under Section 11 of the Animals Act 1971, the term 'livestock' includes (amongst a great many other animals) horses, asses and mules. Consequently, although horses are not strictly agricultural animals (unless they are bred for meat), they do fall within the definition of livestock. The significance of this is that under the the Animals Act, an owner of livestock is strictly liable for damage caused by such livestock if it trespasses onto another owner's land.

Crossing the boundary

It is not clear, in your case, who owns the boundary fence. However, if the boundary fence represents the legal boundary between the two properties, then it is clear that the hedge is situated on the neighbour's land and belongs to the neighbour.

If the hedge is damaged by the horses, then this will amount to trespass. It does not matter whether or not the horses actually walk on the neighbour's land. For trespass to take place, it is sufficient if any part of the animal crosses the boundary, for example by a horse stretching its neck and head over or through a fence or over a ditch.

In these circumstances it is clearly the owner's responsibility to ensure that her horses are unable to stretch over or through the boundary fence and thereby prevent them from eating her neighbour's hedge. This may require either the erection of another protective boundary fence a few feet within her boundary, or, alternatively, the erection of a wire or other physical boundary which will prevent the horses from leaning through or over the existing boundary fence.

Richard Chamberlain

Head high

"ARE THERE ANY SCHOOLING TECHNIQUES TO CALM MY HORSE DOWN?"

Q **My Arab x Connemara is generally very well behaved but she can get very excited when we go forwards to trot. She raises her head and gets faster and faster, until we are out of control.**

She is already ridden in a running martingale and flash noseband. Are there any schooling techniques I can try to calm her down?

A Arabs with problems are more likely to go hollow and hot up than other breeds, but this does not mean that she will never go well. All you have to do is find out where problems stem from, and then start to rebuild her confidence.

It is possible that she may be suffering discomfort, if not pain, when she is being ridden. The fact that she is going forward should rule out unsoundness, although this is always worth checking with your vet. However it is more likely that the root of her discomfort is either in her back or her mouth.

Does your saddle fit?

Arabs (and many Connemaras) are notorious for having very round rib cages. This affects the fit of the saddle, particularly if this is combined with low withers and, therefore, shoulder blades which finish very high up the saddle.

Although possibly not feeling very wide to ride, this necessitates using a wide-fitting saddle to accommodate the fact that the back is widening considerably under the points of the tree. If this has not been sufficiently taken into account when fitting the saddle, the points will pinch and the weight of the rider will, at the same time, be pitched to the back of the saddle.

The resulting uneven distribution of the rider's weight will cause hollowing and rushing away from the source of discomfort. A classic sign that this may have been happening is rub marks towards the back of the saddle area.

You would be well advised to call in an equine therapist, as, sadly, not all saddlers are aware of the problems which may be caused by a slightly tight-fitting saddle. Once this is sorted out, you should notice an immediate improvement in her way of going.

Make her comfortable

A change in bit may not be appropriate, as this is unlikely to be the cause of the problem. In the interests of safety, however, you could try a curb bit as this will have a lowering effect if used correctly. It is important though that you are confident about riding with two sets of reins if you try this.

Once she is comfortable in her back and her mouth, she will be much more able to settle and work happily. Once her muscles have started to develop and relax in the right places, she will be able to accept a softer, calmer way of going.

Keep schooling sessions short for the time being, aiming to do a little successfully rather than too much and waiting for problems to develop. It is always better to finish on a good note. Work hard on your own riding! An ability to ride from leg to hand, maintaining balance whatever the horse does underneath you, and plenty of tact and patience, will be the keys to improvement.

Listen to your mare when she says she is confused and cannot cope. Only when she goes forward and straight in the walk - stretching down if you offer her the rein - should you venture into trot. Stay in walk when you hack out until she will trot calmly at home.

Choose your days carefully when you want to be a little more ambitious. Cold windy days will be when she is at her liveliest. The day folllowing a long hack rather than a day off will have her at her most receptive, especially if the sun is shining and you are relaxed. Things will improve, and a partnership will develop, if you want to put in the effort.

Fliss Gillott

Horse behaving badly

"I THINK MY HORSE IS A RIG..."

Q *"...I bought him as a gelding but he does have a very stallion-like look about him and when I checked his records I discovered that he had only been gelded three years before. A blood test to see whether he is a rig proved negative.*

"He is turned out with a large group of geldings, and the owner of the yard is convinced that he has been terrorising the other horses as a number have already been kicked."

A Rob Pilsworth replies...

Although not unusual for geldings to show abnormal sexual behaviour when they are moved and mixed with a strange group of horses. They may even develop a full erection and even serve a mare in a new field of horses. This situation will also stimulate aggressive, stallion-like behaviour.

This has nothing to do with any residual testicular tissue, and, therefore, hormonal therapy is probably not going to be of benefit. This is a behaviour pattern, which seems to be triggered by social factors, irrespective of whether or not the testicles have been removed.

Tranquilisers
My own advice would be to use a mild tranquiliser when turning your horse out with his new collection of companions. Acetlypromazine (ACP) is available in tablet form from your veterinary surgeon. The tablets fit neatly into the middle of a Polo mint and can, therefore, readily be given by mouth.

Although not specified licensed for use in the horse, your veterinary surgeon could certainly dispense some tablets for your use in this particular situation, as there is no other licensed product available. I would start with a dose of 3 x 25mg tablets, if your horse is a normal size (400 - 500kg), and a lower dose if he is smaller. Give these tablets half an hour before the prospective turnout. This should gently sedate the horse so that he is less keen to join in any 'fisticuffs' going on in the field.

Usually, once horses have got used to each other, the incidence of aggressive and sexual behaviour diminishes rapidly, so, as long as you can get your horse over the first week of life with his companions, you should find little or no trouble. If a new horse is then introduced, things start all over again, so it is important that you try to find a stable livery situation.

Introducing a new companion
Another thing that is often useful if you are intending to turn a horse out with a companion, is to introduce them on a ride, rather than just stick them both out in the field. If you find a friend with a horse you would like to share a field with, tack up both horses and take them out for an hour's exercise, stopping along the way and allowing them to pick at some grass. In this way, they get to smell each other and get to know each other before they are let off the rein.

When you return from the ride, both horses should be relatively tired and not quite so keen on picking a fight. They can then be let off their bridles together in the paddock, and will often be happy to munch grass, as they are familiar with each other's smells at that time.

Hormone therapy
If all of this fails, then one final solution might be to try a drug called Regumate. This is available from your vet and is used to control the reproduction of mares. It is a synthetic progesterone. This is the hormone which is produced during pregnancy in the mare and tends to have a calming effect on horses - the typical placid, serene, pregnant mare!

Although not intended for use in geldings, the drug is licensed for use in the horse, and your vet would, therefore, be able to dispense the

drug. I would use this as a last resort, however, and try behaviour management and the use of ACP tablets as a first step.

Rob Pilsworth

Jane van Lennep replies...

Horses are, by nature, herd animals. Their natural home is wide expanses of plains. They are obligate herbivores, wandering up to 30 miles a day to find enough grazing. Your horse has found himself in a very difficult situation. As I see it, the major part of the problem stems from the fact that these geldings are over-crowded. They have one of their needs fulfilled - they have plenty of company - but food may be in short supply. Under such conditions, there are bound to be fights as they all struggle to secure a better ranking.

Reducing the risk of injury

As an immediate measure, all hind shoes should be removed before any serious injury occurs. If this is not done, and there is serious injury, then I have to say that I would regard this as negligence. If the group size cannot be reduced when the grass is in short supply, then hay could be provided in the field to help take the heat out of the situation.

Very many geldings exhibit behaviour also seen in stallions. Especially when they are in new company, they will show off and strut about, to establish how they will fit in with their new companions. They may even get in scraps and minor fights as part of that process. It does not mean that they are dangerous or some sort of semi-stallion. It means they are a horse, doing the things that horses do!

So where do you go from here? Turning him out with one other in a tiny paddock has to be better for your horse than being in the stable all day. At least he will have something else to look at, some fresh air and the chance to socialise. Until the large group of geldings is disarmed by removing all the hind shoes, then your chap is probably safer not being with them. You are going to need to exercise some good diplomatic skills at the yard, firstly with the yard owner, and then with all the other owners, possibly calling a full meeting of all the owners.

Managing without hind shoes

Here in the UK, we are illogically attached to the need for hind shoes, and curiously blind to the terrible damage they inflict. In fact, it is pretty rare for a horse to need hind shoes. The hind feet are slightly more upright than the front feet, and more angular, so they are less likely to split. The horse carries more weight naturally on the front feet, even when they are schooled to take equal weight, or even more weight on the hinds when ridden.

When I had a lot of liveries, most of the owners were happy to have their horses unshod on the hinds in order to get the benefit of extra grazing without risking serious injury. The biggest tragedy was when one horse was moved to another yard where hind shoes were allowed. Within weeks, the poor horse had a fractured hock and a promising endurance career was shattered, too.

You may have a mountain to climb, but you have choices, too. Not least your choice of livery yard for your horse.

Jane van Lennep

The value of grazing

"WHAT IS THE NUTRITIONAL CONTENT OF GRASS?"

Q **How do you assess the contribution that grass makes to the daily feed ration in terms of weight and nutritional content when a horse is turned out all day, then turned out by day and stabled by night?**

A The contribution of the grazing is very hard to assess in scientific terms, as there are so many variables.

The quality of grazing varies through the year, building quickly to a peak in early June, then tailing off until the rain comes in the autumn when it has another little surge, usually in September. It then tails off again and stops growing altogether over the worst months of the winter. Remaining grass at this time is not usually of a very good feed value, but is still a source of fresh food and all-important fibre.

A horse living out full-time on well-managed pasture will gain weight in the summer and lose weight in the winter. This suggests that summer grass more than supplies its needs and in the winter, fails to meet them.

Some very good doers, turned out by day in summer, will need very little extra feed overnight. For others, a reasonable starting point is that the grazing is equivalent to the hay they would have eaten, had they been in the stable with ad-lib hay.

In the summer, grazing is usually equivalent to hay and short feed, and full-time grazing can provide enough energy for maintenance and light to medium work. In the winter, however, grazing is equivalent to just hay if there is grass of any reasonable quality. Bear in mind also that being unrugged in bad weather causes weight loss to the horse, due to the energy the animal needs to keep warm.

As a rule of thumb, horses naturally eat for 12 to 16 hours a day; so six to eight hours' grazing could provide half their total needs. But in the end, it is up to the owner or whoever cares for the horse to anticipate the changes to the grazing and act in time – for instance, instigating winter or extra feeding before there is a weight loss in the autumn.

A good horse keeper will also notice changes in the horse's condition and act promptly, adjusting supplementary feeding as required to maintain an even weight on the horse.
Jane Van Lennep

Bang, bang, bang...

"MY MARE WON'T STOP BANGING THE STABLE DOOR!"

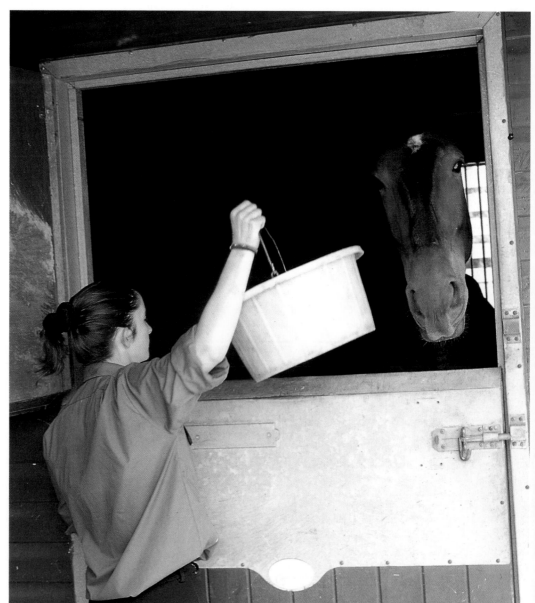

Q **Is there any way I can stop my mare banging her stable door at the crack of dawn, before the neighbours start complaining?**

A Most of the problem behaviour that arises in horses is the result of miscommunication. In this case the horse has learned to anticipate a pleasurable situation that occurs each morning - that is the arrival of you and food!

Why does she do it?

As part of the learning process, your horse has made certain associations that enable her to predict what will happen. In her case, it seems likely that she has learnt that your arrival, and the arrival of her food, is associated with the arrival of daylight. In the winter this would be around 7am, but in the summer it's more like 5am!

The door banging is all part of her anticipatory response. As her internal cues (glucose levels, etc) all start to get stronger, so does her motivation to consume food.

In order to alleviate the need to find food to satisfy her motivational state, your mare will begin to show species-typical food searching movements (moving around more, exploring, nosing etc), but she is unable to do her natural behaviour because the stable door is in the way. The door banging is just her response to the door, and, of course, it is rewarded each day, because in her eyes she is rewarded for banging due to you feeding her eventually!

Once you understand why your horse bangs her door, and also how it has become reinforced, it is slightly easier to deal with.

How can you deal with it?

Firstly, for your neighbours' sake, and for the sake of your horse's joints, I suggest you pad the door well, to prevent the noise and the potential injuries.

Then you must start to work on ways of re-training your horse so that she does not use door banging to attract attention or as a precursor to the arrival of her food.

Give the horse a food reward for more appropriate behaviour, such as standing quietly, and negatively reinforce the door banging by withdrawing food - of course this means that initially the horse will bang even more, so you must make sure she is bandaged and the door is well padded. This will obviously take time and dedication on your part.

I also suggest that you find a way of keeping your horse occupied in her stable so that the internal cues are altered; for example, giving her more hay may ensure that she is not extremely hungry in the morning.

Some people even use an electronically controlled feed hopper that drops food at a particular time each morning that coincides with daylight. This enables the horse to have more control over its living environment, although it can lead to other problems, amd one has to be careful to maintain the equipment!

I have found that some horses will use an empty feeding ball - which trickles feed out slowly - as an outlet for their drive to feed, and this occupies them until the ball is refilled.

However, the method you choose whould depend on what works best for you and your horse, but there are plenty of ideas here!

Natalie Waran

Putting up a fight

"LIFE IS JUST ONE LONG BATTLE WITH MY HORSE."

Q I've tried schooling my five-year-old cob and we're okay on the ground together, but he takes no notice of me - or my instructor - when I get on board. He's also very stong and I've had to try a number of bits to control him. What should I do, as life with him seems to be one long battle?

A Firstly, the solution to the problem lies with the rider, not the horse. Fighting tends to develop from misunderstanding and a lack of training, or an inablility to do what is asked through physical causes. If there is a physical reason for your horse being unhappy and out of control, talk to a specialist - someone who can see him at rest as well as at work.

Most youngsters need their backs looked at as they become accustomed to the new pressures put on them with starting work. You will also need to get your saddle checked for fit, as the horse may well have changed shape with his developing maturity.

Back to basics
Assuming all is well physically and bearing in mind that your horse is a willing pupil from the ground, his temperament is probably also suited to being a riding horse. The problem then is rooted in training. When you talk to him from the ground, he can see you and may be responding to your body language as well as your voice. Once on his back, you disappear from view and he is denied this support of your voice commands.

To teach him to respond to legs, weight, back, seat and hand aids, take him through the basics of training with an assistant on the ground, who should be able to lunge him and take over the role that you have had in doing work from the ground. But don't attempt to do any more than walk, turn and halt until he is totally responsive to the aids.

When you are both ready to start trotting again, keep it short, working on your transitions and keeping his attention while he is trotting.

Schooling solutions
To make him attentive, put out some markers when you are schooling, then, as well as riding round an oblong arena, bend in and out of the markers, turning alternately left and right, while still allowing him time to work out what you are asking before each turn. Ride circles, loops, figures of eight and so on. Stop occasionally to give him a break and a chance to stretch his neck. Do as much as you can with legs and weight, as as little as possible with your rein aids to encourage him to be soft and light in his mouth. Doing these simple but varied exercises a little faster when the time is right should take you into a slow trot, maintaining the continuity of what you have already done.

Aim to build a partnership based on understanding and reward for good behaviour. There will be times when your horse gets strong and wants to go faster, but even then, his basic schooling will come into play so that he is not totally out of control. Use whichever bit you feel happiest with - it is your hands which dictate how severe the effect will be on his mouth.

Finally, is your instructor prepared to put in some time with him to get to the root of the problem? If she is, then stay with her. If, on the other hand, she is blaming your very inexperienced young horse for being 'bad', maybe you should have a rethink.
Fliss Gillott

Farrier fears

"MY HORSE HAS TO BE SEDATED WHEN SHOD."

Q My horse has to be sedated to be shod! I recently bought a little cob who had been bred by gypsies. He is a lovely horse, but he will not be shod and has to be sedated. He doesn't like picking up his feet, particularly the near hind. He either tries to walk off or stamps his foot down hard.

A The easiest explanation for your horse's unwillingness to co-operate is that he doesn't understand what you want from him, because he has not been taught the behaviour. If this is likely to be the case, then we need to realise that much of his misbehaviour is likely to result from confusion, frustration and possibly fear.

He has now learned that when someone tries to pick up his feet, he should walk away or stamp them down hard, and then they will stop. The fact that you have managed to have him shod whilst sedated does not mean that he should accept the situation next time, since it is fairly well documented that, although animals/people are calmer when sedated, they don't learn anything during that time.

Physical checks
My main concern is that you mention that he is particularly reluctant to lift a certain hoof. I realise that you may have had the horse vetted prior to buying him, but it might be worth having his hindlegs checked again. It may be that your horse initially objected to this particular leg being lifted for good reason, perhaps it was painful, or perhaps he has injured that leg previously.

It is always a good idea when dealing with any behavioural problem to ask your vet to check that there is no obvious physical reason for the problem.

Teaching step by step
Once you have decided what is most likely to be the reason for your horse's behaviour, and if

necessary treated any physical problem, you will need to go through the process of training him to lift his feet up when you give a particular signal. Then you need to shape his behaviour, which means that you progressively build from one stage of the leg lifting process to the next.

Initially I would suggest you lean against his shoulder and run your hand down his leg, and reward him for standing still. Then lean harder and gently squeeze the fetlock joint and say 'lift' or 'up'. As you lean you will find that eventually he lifts his foot, accidentally at first, which your helper immediately rewards, saying 'good boy' and giving a small food reward, and so on until he is only getting a reward of 'good boy' for picking up his foot and holding it up for a period of 30 seconds.

You will need to do this over a few training sessions, to give him time to learn. Do the same with all four legs, being patient and consistent until he understands the relationships between your signal (squeezing the fetlock and saying 'lift') and his correct behavioural response.

The next stage
Only when you are confident that he understands your signal should you expect him to tolerate being shod... and even then it might be better to shoe only the front feet at first,

leaving the hind ones until another day initially.

It is important that your horse learns to cope with being shod by taking time to teach him that there is nothing to fear. After all, he will have to cope with this procedure every eight or so weeks for the rest of his working life!

Natalie Waran

A case of negligence?

"CAN I CLAIM FOR AN INJURY SUSTAINED AT A LIVERY YARD?"

Q **I recently placed my horse in a livery yard where he was to be prepared for sale, and a prospective purchaser was found. However, before the vetting he came in from the field with a nasty cut on his leg. This injury has required considerable treatment and expense.**

Could I have a case of negligence against the livery yard owner? She says that there is nothing in the field to cause such an injury, although my horse did lose a shoe in the field, which has never been found.

A There are two possible grounds for a claim against the owner of the livery yard arising from these particular circumstances. The first is for a breach of contract and the second is for negligence.

There seems to be little doubt as to the basic terms of the contract. In return for a fee, the owner of the livery yard would provide shelter, grazing and general care of the horse, in addition to training and preparation for sale. This is a contract for services and not a contract for the sale of goods to which the Sale of Goods Act 1979 applies. Consequently, the only question to be determined is whether or not the services were provided in accordance with the agreement. There is no suggestion that this was not the case.

A case for negligence

In order to succeed in a claim for negligence, it is necessary to establish that the owner of the livery yard owed a duty of care to the owner of the horse, that there has been a breach of that duty and that the injury sustained was reasonably foreseeable and arose directly as a result of the breach of the duty of care.

There can be little doubt that the owner of the yard owed a duty of care to look after the horse in a satisfactory and proper manner. It is much harder to determine whether there has

been any breach of this duty.

This will depend very much upon the state and condition of the field into which the horse was turned out, the type of fencing, the existence or absence of any structures or obstacles in the field and the disposition of other horses turned out in the same field.

There is no indication that any of these factors were unsatisfactory or that there was any aspect of the handling and care of the horse and its treatment after the injury which were unsatisfactory or inadequate.

This leaves only the question of how the injury was caused and the possibility that it may have been attributable to the loss of a shoe in the weeks prior to the accident. This is a very small risk, the significance of which will depend to some extent on the size of the turnout field.

Clearly, if the field is large, the risk is very small and the task of finding a lost shoe very difficult, and the task of finding a single nail almost impossible. If the field is smaller, the risk is greater but the task of finding the lost shoe is a little easier.

Establishing the degree of risk

The Courts' approach to such issues is to balance the degree of risk and the seriousness of the consequences that result from it against the expense and effort required in order to minimise or eliminate the risk.

The greater the risk or the seriousness of the consequences, the greater the effort that must be made to reduce such risk.

In this case, the question is whether the risk of injury to a horse and the possible seriousness of such injury were so great that the owner of the livery yard should have made a greater effort to find the lost shoe and nail. If the answer to that question is no, then there will have been no breach of the duty of care and no liability on the owner of the yard.

Unless the field was very small, it is unlikely that the owner of the yard has been in breach of her duty of care in these circumstances. However, if the answer is yes, then the owner of the yard may have been negligent, but it will still be necessary to show that the injury sustained by the horse was reasonably foreseeable and that it was caused by the lost shoe or nail.
Richard Chamberlain

Work for a three-year-old

"AM I WORKING MY FILLY TOO HARD?"

Q **I have a three-year-old Thoroughbred cross filly. I lunge her four times a week for 20 minutes and ride her twice a week for an hour with a break halfway. I am worried because she sometimes nods her head - am I working her too hard?**

A Horses mature at different rates and are capable of doing varied amounts of work according, in part, to their level of maturity. However, three is still very young and I would be very cautious about suggesting how much work your filly could reasonably manage.

As a general rule, we only back our three-year-olds towards the end of the summer and then turn them away again until the following spring, leaving them until they are four before starting any work.

Still growing

At three, the horse is still growing, not necessarily with much more height to make up, but certainly in the frame. The shoulders, for example, are still relatively slight and more upright than they will be at maturity. The difference is similar to a human teenager, who will be gangly in the early teens compared to the stronger, wider frame of adulthood.

Signs of overwork

Lungeing is very hard work for a youngster, especially if most of the lunge work is in trot. The repeated turns put considerable strain on young joints, so you must check carefully after each session for signs of heat or swelling around all joints.

Her head nodding could be a sign that she is finding the work challenging. It will certainly also help to give her a break midway through the hour's hacking, but I would also suggest that you lead her for part of the way, as long it is a safe option.

Discipline

Some youngsters need to work to keep their minds occupied, and to establish some level of discipline before they become too strong and self-assured to be manageable. If this is the case, then to keep them ticking over in light work is a good thing.

Another reason to keep them in work through their three-year-old to four-year-old winter would be if the options for alternative exercise are limited. In other words, light work is better than being confined to the stable.

Ideally, it would probably be better for your filly to be rested through the winter and to start her again early next year. She will then be reaching full maturity and able to begin work more seriously.

Breeds and types vary, but a horse is not usually at its physical peak until about eight years of age, so a gradual increase in work until this time is recommended. For the normal one-horse owner working up to riding club level, you can reckon on six being the age for full work to begin.

Take care to balance how much work she can take physically with how much she needs for mental development and you should have a horse which gives you many years of pleasure.
Fliss Gillott

Laminitis-sweet itch link

"MY RESCUE PONY'S SWEET ITCH HAS RECURRED."

Q When I took on a pony as a rescue case, he was very thin and suffered badly from sweet itch which, incidentally, seems to get worse when he comes into the stable. It has also recurred, causing him to itch like crazy. I don't want to give him steroids as I think that may have caused him to suffer from laminitis, something we discovered at the vetting. As a result, the bones in his front feet have dropped. What should I do to improve his condition?

A As it is impossible to say whether or not the laminitis was caused by steroids, we should look at the role of laminitis in this pony's itchiness – it brings with it pain and an accumulation of toxins.

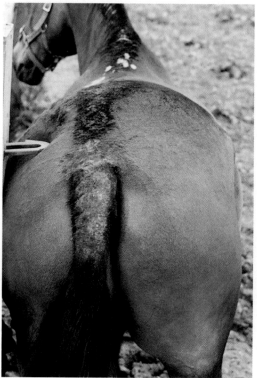

The fact that the pedal bones have dropped means that they will be closer to the ground and, therefore, more susceptible to concussion. To alleviate this, horses and ponies often resort to hunching their shoulders and tightening their back muscles, which places an additional strain on the already overworked muscle metabolism.

Is it behavioural?
Toxins in the body must have somewhere to go – it doesn't always follow that because laminitis is no longer present, the toxins have been eliminated. Not only could the the pony's liver function be impaired through the laminitis and anorexia, but the balance of gut flora may be inadequate, too.

The skin metabolism can only return to normal and cope with environmental challenges and allergens if it receives adequate nutrients. And it will only get these if the digestion is unimpaired.

However, there may be a behavioural element to the itching in the stable, as the pony is happier outdoors. This will be only one piece in the puzzle, but it must be addressed before the jigsaw is complete. Therefore . . .
1. Ensure the pony is shod for maximum comfort.
2. Re-examine the nutrition, especially with reference to the minerals and vitamins.
3. Rebuild a healthy gut flora – for example, using probiotics.
4. Consider using herbs to detoxify the body tissues.
5. Ask a behavioural expert to identify needs in the pony's social behaviour and highlight areas where positive human interaction could help him break the itch/scratch cycle.
Sara Wyche

Trailer trauma

"MY HORSE USED TO BE PERFECT TO LOAD, BUT NOW HE REFUSES TO."

Q **My horse has always loaded perfectly into a trailer, but gradually, he has started to kick up a fuss - now he actually refuses to load. Help!**

A Horses are by nature extremely suspicious of 'trappy', closed and dark 'caverns'. Most trailers and lorries represent the worst kind of environment for animals that have evolved to live in large open spaces. Not only are they expected to put themselves in an extremely life-threatening situation, but they are also expected to deal with the movement, the close presence of another horse, petrol/diesel fumes, temperature extremes, humidity problems and lack of airflow. When something goes wrong, it's difficult to tell exactly which of these factors may have been a problem.

We can only make some assumptions about what happened on the day your horse refused to load. You don't say how old your horse is or if he was with another horse. In addition, what was the driving like and were there any obvious incidents during the journey? Maybe his travel mate redirected his or her frustration on to him. He may have found that on this particular journey, his limbs were more taxed by trying to balance in the trailer.

All of these may explain his unwillingness to re-enter the trailer. Of course, having made the association between the trailer and feeling bad, he was therefore determined not to put himself into the situation again!

What can you do?

First make sure there is no physical explanation for his behaviour. For example, if he has a problem with his back, he may well dislike travelling, since this does rely on a lot of balancing effort, which involves the muscles in the back. Once you are satisfied he is physically fine, then first make sure he is sufficiently motivated to work for your praise and food rewards (try doing some work on leading him forward willingly).

Next find somewhere you can back the trailer up to, where the ramp can be level, and make a pen at the bottom of the ramp so that your horse cannot escape. You can use a 'buddy' horse in the box to encourage him to load, but it may not be necessary. Give yourself plenty of time, arm yourself with lots of carrots and be prepared to reward him when he makes a move

towards the ramp, sniffs the ramp, etc, until eventually he puts a foot on the ramp. Since he has nowhere to go but up the ramp - and food comes when he makes the right moves - he will soon learn a new response.

Once you have led him in the trailer a few times and had the engine on the car running, you should then take him for a short drive, preferably with another horse. Check that driving speed and smoothness are a priority, so you don't confirm his belief that trailers are frightening!

You need to spend time with your horse and work out what it is that is worrying him. Be firm and consistent, and reward his good behaviour - ignoring him when he is stroppy. It will take time but, of course, it will be worth it in the end.
Natalie Waran

Sitting trot

"HOW CAN I STOP MY HORSE HOLLOWING WHEN I TAKE SITTING TROT?"

Q **Every time I go from rising to sitting trot my horse raises his head and hollows his back.**

A In theory, it should make no difference to the horse whether the rider is in sitting or rising trot. The horse is the only thing keeping the entire weight of the rider off the ground, so that even when the rider stands up in the stirrups, some part of the horse's back is still weight bearing.

What does make a difference is the rider's ability or otherwise, to sit still in the saddle. An unbalanced rider may thump down during rising trot, but is likely to cause even more discomfort by bumping around in sitting trot. A good rider is no hindrance to the horse at all in sitting trot, so if you have a horse which hollows when you sit, then you have a responsibility to learn to sit correctly. This is very much a rider problem rather than a horse problem!

There is plenty of incentive to get to grips with sitting trot. The fine tuning which is required to get the very best from your horse cannot be done if you spend half your time out of the saddle. It also means that you will end up using far more leg than is either desirable or necessary because you are unable to use your seat effectively. This effect runs into canter and the walk through poorly ridden transitions as well, apart from the fact that a good seat is needed in all the gaits.

Sit tall

Sitting correctly in the walk is much easier than sitting correctly in the trot, simply because there is less bounce. However, it is in the walk that you need to start perfecting your position. It is particularly important to sit tall, maintaining the natural slight hollow in the back without stiffness.

Only tense the muscles needed to maintain posture and balance as well as the forward

movement of the horse. Keep your abdominal muscles stretched to counter any tendency to collapse and hunch up when the horse moves into trot.

The really crucial part of your anatomy is your seat. Allow the pelvis to absorb the movement of the walk whilst remaining upright, not tilting either forwards or backwards. In the walk, the horse's back has a lot of side to side movement, which you will feel increase as you accept the movement in your seat/pelvis/lower back area. Your seat bones all this time remain pressing gently but firmly straight down into the saddle.

Ask for trot when your horse is well prepared to trot, not from a lot of pushing and shoving on your part. It is much easier to ride well if you do not have to work too hard. Maintain the position you had in walk. It may help to tilt your pelvis very slightly back if your horse has a big trot so that you do not get 'left behind' or if you feel that you have a tendency to get 'bounced' up the back of the saddle.

Only trot a short distance and keep the trot quite slow and in a steady rhythm. It requires a lot of concentration to sit still and remain supple if you are in the habit of feeling uncomfortable. Short spells of concentration are much easier to maintain, and your confidence in your ability to sit properly in sitting trot will improve if you make sure of success.

Help your horse to help you
As far as the horse is concerned, it is easy to ride well (relatively!) on a well schooled and comfortable horse. The better the horse, the better the rider, and the better the rider, the better the horse. So it is important to encourage your horse to work well at the same time as improving your seat. Make quite sure that your horse is working in a correct outline in walk, and that, through a well ridden transition, this outline is maintained into the trot.

Keep the trot slow so that you have a better chance of being able to sit still and therefore ride effectively, which in turn means you have the opportunity to keep the horse round in his outline.

Once you have been able to establish good results in short, slow trots, you feel a lot more confident about being able to keep everything together for longer spells. From here start to increase impulsion, but always, always retaining the steady deep seat in the saddle, absorbing not resisting the movement. Stretch your abdomen up and forward while your legs stay long down the horse's sides.

Maintain a positive image
It is possible to concentrate on more than one thing at a time, which is why it is so helpful to sort your weaknesses out one step at a time in the slower gait of walk. Once you can pinpoint exactly what it is that you do wrong which inhibits your ability to work your horse correctly, then you will be able to focus on that one thing while you are in sitting trot. Carrying on regardless when things fall apart will reinforce mistakes as well as causing misery to your poor horse.

Work really hard on reinforcing the positive aspects of your work and thus sow the seeds of success. Having a phrase or an image in your mind that you can keep repeating will help your concentration. Perhaps this could be to sit down or sit tall, think forward and up, soften your seat like a half-inflated balloon - or keep a mental image of someone like Carl Hester whose posture is superb.

You will have time to focus on and improve your horse once you are comfortable and confident in your ability to sit to the trot. Get the horse to help you, and you will be able to help him in turn.

Fliss Gillott

Winter warmth

"DOES MY HORSE REALLY NEED A TURNOUT RUG?"

Q I own a four-year-old Shire x Friesian gelding who is turned out part of the day. I am considering leaving him unrugged when he is turned out. However, will he need to wear a rug in his stable where he can't move around so easily to keep warm?

Because my horse is rather hairy he can be a bit sweaty when we get back from a ride. I would like to know the best way to dry him off, or whether it would be better to give him a bib clip, in which case would I need to keep him rugged up all the time?

A A layer of warm air under a horse's thick winter coat helps to keep a horse warm. If the horse is warm, the coat lies flat and smooth, making the air layer smaller. If the horse gets cold, erector muscles in the hair follicle contract and make the hair stand up, increasing the air space. However, rugging could suppress the amount of coat your horse grows.

If the stable is not draughty, it may be better not to rug him. Although he cannot move around so much to keep warm, you must consider that, on the other hand, he does not need to move around to keep warm because he is indoors. However, be prepared to rug him if it gets really awful and he is getting cold.

Drying off

A horse should not be left until he is dry. However, if a horse is clearly drying off well, is not at all cold, or still sweating, is cleaned up following your ride and is eating his hay, then I personally do not think he will come to too much harm if he is then left. Perhaps the answer is to go back later to make quite sure the horse is as well as when you left him.

Sweat rugs are designed to help dry wet horses. They are not intended to be used on their own. The sweat rug should have a cotton sheet, eg a summer sheet, over the top of it to trap a layer of air.

Obviously, you will walk at the end of your ride, but you may need to do more walking in hand. Allowing the horse to roll is an excellent way of getting him to relax and stop sweating. Allowing him to drink not only replaces lost fluids, but cools him down as well.

After a ride, you could remove any mud, grease etc, by spongeing as well as brushing. Put him in the paddock for a short while, while you get yourself sorted out, then get him back in to finish cleaning and tidying him up. You should find he dries off quickly. If the weather is absolutely vile, and he comes back from his ride cold, then you may find a rug helps, perhaps a modern 'breathable' type.

Clipping

I have successfuly kept horses with bib clips out most of the time and not rugged. A bib clip removes a strip of coat from the gullet, between the jaws and to the chin at the top, whilst at the bottom, it widens to take out the front of the chest, goes between the legs and stops at the back edge of the girth.

When the weather gets too awful to ride at all, your lucky horse will be cosy and happy in the clothes nature gave him, and he will be easier for you to care for, too!

Jane van Lennep

71

Reflex action

"DOES MY PONY HAVE A SORE BACK?"

Q **My pony was diagnosed with a sore back after the vet ran a coin along his spine. The pony dipped when this was done and he was subsequently treated with physiotherapy. However, I noticed that my other horses dipped in the same way when I ran a coin down each of their spines. Is this the normal reflex action, as none of the others show signs of having a back problem?**

A The behaviour you are describing is a reflex activity which is completely normal for all horses to exhibit - in fact, all of the following reflex actions are normal.

● If you pinch the horse firmly with a finger and thumb either side of the withers, it should dip its spine.

● If you run a coin or ballpoint pen along either side of the spine, then not only should the horse dip its back but it should flex it laterally to the side on which the stimulation is being performed.

● If you pinch the horse or press firmly with a coin at the tail base, the horse should raise its back.

Where you may have got confused is that these reflex behaviour patterns are employed by vets when assessing a horse for back pain. In other words, a horse with a primary back problem will often show an unwillingness to dip the back in response to firm stimulation.

Alternatively, he may show a 'menace' response or a pain response which is abnormal for the amount of pressure applied to the spine. This is probably what you were observing when your pony was being examined.

However, what is normal and what is not normal in these reflex responses is a field which is often unclear. Many horses will show quite marked menace response to back stimulation as part of their normal behaviour. This will often vary from day to day, so it is a case of getting to know your own horse and how easily it dips and flexes its back on stimulation. What is normal behaviour for one horse may be abnormal for another.

Rob Pilsworth

Not a novice ride

"MY HORSE WAS SOLD TO ME AS A QUIET RIDE - BUT SHE IS ANYTHING BUT!"

Q I am a nervous, novice rider and recently bought my first horse, described as a '...very, very quiet ride, super traffic, box etc...' I went to the stud to try the horse; I asked if I could take her out on the road, but they said a lot of new signs had just been put up which might scare her. However, the vendors assured me that she was a suitable first horse so I decided to buy her.

On getting her home I have found her to be quite sharp and she has been very nervous on the road. I spoke to the stud about this and they said to keep persevering with her. Things came to a head when I was riding on the road with a friend. My horse got very nervous and kicked my friend's horse and bucked me off; I ended up in hospital with a broken back. I would like to know what course of action I should take now?

A Your problem raises two distinct and separate issues. The first is whether or not a claim can successfully be brought against the vendor with regard to the incorrect description applied to the horse. The second is whether or not a claim can be brought against the vendor of the horse with regard to the injury sustained.

Sale of Goods Act

You state that you bought the horse from a stud which indicates the vendor may have been a dealer. In such circumstances the Sale of Goods Act 1979 will apply and under Section 14 of the act the horse would have to be of satisfactory quality, taking into account its age and fitness for the purpose for which it was being sold. The description of the horse was clearly intended to convey that the horse was calm and sensible under saddle and when ridden on the roads.

You advised the vendor before purchase that you were a nervous, novice rider and the vendor appears to have assured you that the horse was a suitable first horse for you to buy.

A misleading description

It's clear that your experience of the horse was completely at odds with the advertised description and assurances given at the time of purchase. The horse was clearly extremely nervous in traffic and very easily alarmed when being ridden out.

The reason given by the vendor for refusing your request to ride the horse out on the road before purchase appears to indicate that the vendor was aware of the horse's nervousness and unreliability in traffic.

In seems clear that the horse was not fit for the purpose for which it was being sold and you would be entitled to return the horse and to demand a refund of the purchase price.

The only difficulty in this respect is if a long period of time has elapsed since it became clear that the horse was not a quiet ride nor safe in traffic. Then there is a possibility that the right to rescind the contract may have been lost by a delay.

In such circumstances you will be entitled to recover damages for the breach of contract, being the difference in value between the horse as it is and the horse as it should have been had it been entirely as described.

A case of misrepresentation

Even if the vendor was not a dealer it is likely that the misdescription of the horse was such that you will have the same right to rescind the contract or to claim damages under Section 2 of the Misrepresentation Act 1967.

This provides that if a vendor makes untrue or misleading representations of fact and the purchaser relies upon those representations and would not otherwise have bought the horse, then the purchaser may be entitled to rescind the contract and demand a refund of the purchase price or alternatively may be entitled to damages.

Claiming for damages

A possible claim for the injuries sustained as a result of your fall is much more difficult to determine. If, as seems likely, the vendor knowingly sold a horse which was extremely nervous when ridden out in traffic to a nervous and inexperienced rider, then they may well be liable in negligence for injury sustained as a result of the horse's violent reaction to traffic or some other stimulus when being ridden out. However you do not indicate any cause for the horse's behaviour at the time. Furthermore, you were already well aware of the horse's disposition and extreme nervousness when being ridden out.

This raises the issue of contributory negligence although the vendor's earlier telephone advice to persevere may limit the extent to which blame may be apportioned to you. Nevertheless, the personal injury claim will be much more difficult to pursue and I would advise you to seek further expert legal advice regarding both claims.
Richard Chamberlain

Late starter

"MY HORSE WON'T LET ME GET ON HIM!"

Q **I recently bought an eight-year-old Arab who had only just been backed and gelded before being turned away for a couple of months. He refuses to let me get on him - he swings away with little regard to what is in his way - objects or people. I cannot get him near the mounting block at all.**

I have had his back, saddle and teeth checked and he has no problems. If I do manage to get on him, he will work happily.

A Your horse is obviously getting himself worked up into a state where he is showing little regard for his own safety, let alone yours. As long as this continues, the problem will not be resolved. He is repeatedly giving himself good reason to panic because his behaviour creates further problems.

When a horse has been through as much as he has, it is not surprising that he is tense and unhappy. Until last year he was full of the joys of his own existence as a stallion. Being gelded as a mature horse is a shock to the system, from which time is needed to recover. If the operation was followed quickly by being backed, he may associate the backing with a feeling of confusion.

Being backed as a mature animal is as much of a change to a horse's life as being gelded, albeit in a different way. What you have now is the equivalent to a just backed three-year-old with hang-ups!

Step by step
Break the process of mounting down into its component parts and sort them out one at a time.

The first step is to teach him to stand while you play around tightening the girth, adjusting your stirrups from the ground, and generally

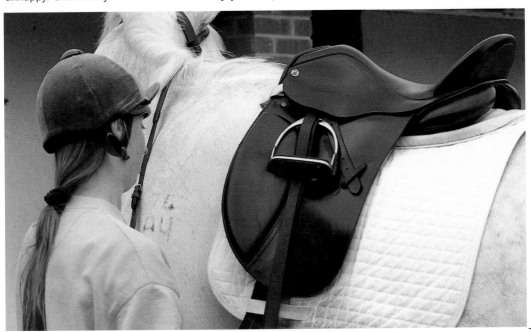

getting ready to mount up. Try to do this on your own, so that he learns to behave like a gentleman because he wants to please you and not because he is forced to.

Be firm with your horse if he moves off, especially if he is pushy, and make much of him when he stands well. He should remain standing while you move around in front of him to get to the other side and back again. When he does this for the first time, return him to the box and reward him for being good. This may take five minutes, it may take several sessions, but it is important that he does it properly.

The next step is to take him to the mounting block without getting on. You may have to lead him past to begin with and halt close by. Make sure he is relaxed when he stands and respects your personal space. Again, do this on your own so that he is not intimidated and forced to fight.

Get him to the block in easy stages, taking as many sessions as are needed. You could perhaps lead him up to it for a small feed - sit on it yourself so that he is no longer tense when he is near it. Avoid even attempting to mount up until he is absolutely ready.

Even after all this, your horse may still try and disappear when you stand up on the mounting block. If you have managed to teach him, on your own, to stand by the block while you are on the ground, then you should be able to bring in a friend to help.

Your next step is to get him used to your being up a level, which could easily be done from a bucket or a portable mounting block. Your friend could hold his head while you do this, and offer him a reward when he stands. Give him lots of pats and words of encouragement from your heightened position, still without mounting up. Only when he is quite relaxed, standing with someone by his head, and with you up in the air on your block, even leaning across the saddle, will he be ready for you to slip into the saddle.

Breaking the cycle

It is vital that you break the chain of events that have led him to being in this state of panic. With time and patience on your side, and a willingness to learn on his, you will succeed. You need to be firm but not bullying. He needs to be reassured within a framework of sympathy, discipline and reward to build up his trust.

It is possible that you will always have to take care getting into the saddle for the first time each day, but that is not a big price to pay. You may have to resort to being legged up while he walks forward until the problem is sorted out. As long as you do not let others talk you into bullying him, you will find a way of coping so that you can both enjoy your ridden work in the future.

Fliss Gillott

Rehab problems

"I THINK MY HORSE HATES ME!"

Q I acquired a Anglo Arab mare a month ago. She is in her late teens and was a 'rescue case'. She has been badly treated in the past, but I have only shown her kindness. She is well fed, so that physically, she has improved enormously. But the problem is she seems to hate me and shows aggression towards me and other horses. What can I do to improve the situation?

A I can understand how it must feel when a horse, that you are doing so much for, does not immediately repay your kindness. However, your horse is not deliberately trying to alienate you - she is looking after herself.

A question of survival
As with all living creatures, the main function of behaviour is to enable the animal to survive, and an animal must use its knowledge of the world around it, which has been acquired throughout its lifetime, to enable it to do this.

You mention that the horse is in her late teens, was in poor condition and has been badly handled. Of course, all these factors will influence her responses to her environment. Lack of knowledge of other horses, will lead her to fear social groups, because she doesn't know how to communicate properly.

Her previous experience of humans will tell her not to trust them! Her previous lack of proper care will make her particularly defensive over her food, and her personal space, just like any animal or person who has been previously deprived.

A question of time

You say that you have had your mare for only a month, and I hope that you can see now that your mare's behavioural responses have been developing over the past 15 or so years, and it will take some time to teach her that things will be different with you.

I certainly think that you will need to cater to some of her preferences. For example, it may be too much to expect her to build a lot of new relationships with a group of horses at her age, and so keeping her with a kindly, elderly pony will be better for her. She may also need you to respect her space in the stable, and heed her warnings to keep away.

Alternatively, you could begin to teach her that if she wants food from you, then she must tolerate being handled, by starting gradually and being consistent.

Think about each situation in the way that she might....*and don't take her behaviour personally*. She doesn't hate you, she fears you. It's up to you to teach her that you will be kind, firm and consistent and gradually, over time, you will build a strong relationship. She will learn to predict your behaviour, and you will learn about hers.

Natalie Waran

Locking stifle

"MY MARE DRAGS A HIND LEG."

Q **When I pick up my mare's hind leg, she jerks it upwards and I have seen her dragging her near hind for a couple of steps as she walks off.**

A The condition you describe is almost certainly upward fixation of the patella. The horse has evolved a system in the hindlimb which allows it to stand on one hind leg and relax the other without consciously thinking about it. This is what is happening when you see a horse standing with a heel cocked-up behind, dozing. In this way, horses are able to sleep standing up which gives them a significant advantage in terms of avoiding predators in the wild, so they are already in position to run, should the situation arise.

Stay apparatus
This is made possible because of the arrangement of the ligaments to the patella (knee cap). There are three ligaments, which come from the patella to the top of the tibia, transferring the pull of the muscles of the thigh to the top of the tibia.

The horse has evolved a bone structure which allows it to 'hook' two of the ligaments going to the top of the patella over one end of the femur. Once this loop of ligament is in position, when the horse puts weight on the leg, the loop simply locks over the end of the femur like a piece of string over a toggle. The horse doesn't have to think about it, and doesn't have to maintain significant muscular contractions to remain standing in this way. It then rests the other leg, and balances on the stable 'tripod'.

The bad news is that in order to free the patella off, the horse has to make a conscious movement to relax the musculature and allow the patella to slip off the 'peg'. Some horses seem to have a problem in this respect, in that they find it difficult to unlock their 'stay apparatus'.

When the patella is locked into place, as the

horse tries to walk forward, it is obviously unable to lift the limb as all the joints are linked together. This gives you the typical, stiff-legged, toe drag that you are describing. Similarly, when you attempt to pick the hindlimb up, you will initially meet a resistance as the patella locking mechanism tightens. This will then fly off rapidly, allowing the leg to suddenly flex.

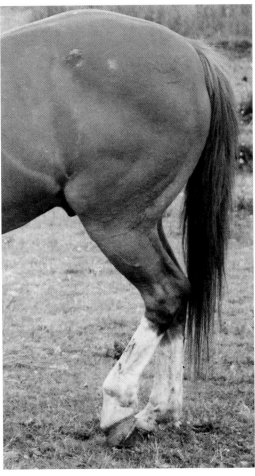

Potential solutions

There are several ways of dealing with this problem. Firstly, horses often lock the patella when they are out of full work. This condition will disappear as they become fully toned up and fit. If the horse is fully fit and continues to lock the stifle, then the next step is to fit plastic heel wedges on both hind legs. These heel wedges are less than a centimetre high, but will usually effect a cure in most horses by simply altering the angle which the leg is held in at rest.

Once plastic heel wedges have been fitted, unfortunately you will have to maintain the horse in them permanently. If they are removed after a long period, the suspensory apparatus 'misses' the support these wedges give. Therefore, this is not something to be undertaken lightly.

Finally, if all else fails, it is possible to perform a surgical operation on one of the patellar ligaments which will prevent the horse being able to lock its stifle. This surgical procedure involves cutting the ligament on the inside of the thigh (medial patellar ligament).

This surgery was done frequently in the past, but gradually we have become aware of the fact that, as with everything in nature, this ligament probably serves a useful purpose. Cutting it is, therefore, not in the best interests of the horse, and it is now well documented that some horses treated in this way, over time, go on to develop fragmentation of the patella which can result in lameness.

As usual, nature is better than we are at deciding what the structure of the horse should be, and if at all possible, we should aid her in this respect by getting the horse fit, and using heel wedges, rather than resorting to surgery.
Rob Pilsworth

Regaining confidence

"MY HORSE IS BEHAVING JUST AS PEOPLE EXPECT HIM TO."

Q A year ago, I purchased a 13-year-old Thoroughbred gelding, with whom I competed successfully at show jumping. Several people said they knew my horse and that he used to be very nappy, and wouldn't jump, but at the time I thought they had confused him with another horse. However, now I am finding that he is behaving exactly as they said and is also very nappy out on hacks – so much so that sometimes I have to get off and lead him. Please help!

A The difficulties you are experiencing with your horse appear to have been induced by other people's comments. I do not think it is mere coincidence that everything was fine until you heard how your horse used to behave. Horses are extraordinarily sensitive to the slightest change in the rider's moods and behaviour, more so if these changes trigger earlier memories.

All through life, we build up scenarios for the various events which happen on a regular basis. This can be anything from getting dressed to driving your car or fetching your horse from the field. We expect one event to be followed by another – either through our own actions or that of another person. The alarm goes off, you turn it off and get out of bed. You don't think hard about this as you know automatically what happens next.

Starting over

Automatic responses for things which happened way back in the past can be restarted by the first move. As an example, do you forget how to ride a bike after 20 years or how to swim after a long break? Or do you remember as soon as you make the first push on the pedal, or push away from the side of the pool and feel the water take your weight?

What may have happened with your horse when you first bought him was that you made a fresh start with him, writing a new 'scenario'. Your approach was new to him, you were trusting, confident and rode without doubting his ability to perform for you. Once a number of people had sown the seeds of doubt in your mind, a hesitation, a tension or maybe even overcompensation may have changed the way you rode. This may then have triggered a sequence of events by starting up an old

'scenario', one in which he backed off then got into trouble. He may have some pretty bad memories coming back to the surface. Sadly, your previous relationship with him is now finished and you will need a lot of patience to get him back to where he was. But it can be done!

Remember when...

Horses have long memories. At the moment for you, this is unfortunate, but just as he could not forget what happened to him before you bought him, he will not have forgotten how things were when all was well. It would take up too much space to go through exactly how to bring about a change.

However, if you can try to find the point at which things start to fall apart, this will be your starting point for putting things right again. Look at it as a crossroads. Where the old you was confident, he went one way. Where the doubting you was hesitant (or over-riding?), he went the other. You want him to slip into the good scenario and not the bad, and it may well work out that one slight change is the only difference needed to put him on the right road again.

Read up

There is an excellent book about developing the right mental approach to successful riding called *"That Winning Feeling"*, by Jane Savoie, published by J A Allen. Monty Roberts tackles the subject in *"Join-Up, Horse Sense for People"* from HarperCollins, looking at some of the psychological aspects of communication between people and horses. Two very different books, but either could help you through this patch. You had your horse going well before, so you can do it again. You know it is possible, and you know there is no physical reason to hold back. With this knowledge, you can rebuild your own confidence. Be patient – you can do it.
Fliss Gillott

Feeding an old-timer

"WHAT CAN I FEED MY VETERAN PONY?"

Q My 36-year-old, 14hh Native pony's teeth are now so poor that he cannot eat hay and the grazing is too short for him in winter. At present, he is surviving on a mixture of AlfaBeet, Alfa-A and Baileys No 1. Please could you suggest a diet that is well-balanced, has sufficient roughage and is reasonably priced?

A Your pony is lucky to have such a caring owner to take care of him – and providing him with a suitable diet is vital in helping him in his dotage.

You are presently using AlfaBeet, which is an excellent feed, especially for older horses. It is a combination of unmolassed sugar beet and alfalfa (or lucerne). You could save money straightaway by buying unmolassed sugar beet separately and soaking this with lucerne/alfalfa pellets. As straight ingredients, you should be able to get these cheaper.

The only difference you will find in practical terms is that the unmolassed sugar beet pellets will need longer to soak than your AlfaBeet. They should be soaked for up to 24 hours and need more water than ordinary sugar beet, which is molassed. Once soaked, the pieces will look larger than the soaked AlfaBeet, but they should still be all right for your pony to eat.

Alfa-A is chopped, dried, molassed lucerne. Instead of this, to save money, you could just use more of the lucerne pellets. As a further economical feed with good levels of fibre, you could try grass pellets. These have a higher feed value than lucerne or sugar beet, but are very economical. They usually come in 20kg bags.

How much to feed?

If your 14hh pony weighs in at around 350kg, his intake of feed on a dry-matter basis will be about 8kg per day (horses need 2-2.5 per cent of body weight in food per day). In terms of actual feed value, this amount of feed, using the

ingredients I have suggested, will deliver around 70-80 MegaJoules, which is well in excess of maintenance for a pony that size (in the order of 45 MJ), but this pony will need lots of extra nourishment. His digestion will be less efficient and he will need more food to keep warm in the winter. Winter weather can create as much need for nourishment as hard work.

You could meet this pony's needs very well with, say, 3kg per day of lucerne pellets, 3kg per day of grass pellets and 2kg per day of unmolassed sugar beet. If he is able to get some benefit from the grazing, then you can reduce accordingly. A bag of lucerne pellets will last you just over eight days, as will the grass nuts. A bag of sugar beet should go 10 days.

This diet is fairly high in protein, but it is all from forages, which is the natural form. As he is now so elderly, your pony will need extra protein, but this diet is still perfectly safe for any horse. All the feeds suggested are high in good-quality fibre, which your pony will be able to use to keep warm, maintain his weight and hopefully keep as healthy as a 36-year-old can. The diet also delivers a lot of calcium, which is important to help keep his old bones strong.

The only thing in less than plentiful amounts is oil. Horses do not need very much of this, but a little more than the minimum of suitable oil can enhance a horse's condition and improve the coat in a way that nothing else can. So if your budget can run to it, add a little vegetable oil or, ideally, some linseed.

Jane van Lennep

Stress mangement

"HOW CAN I KEEP MY HORSE SANE WHEN HE IS RESTRICTED TO HIS STABLE?"

Q At present I am having to keep my horse in his stable for 24 hours a day as he is prone to laminitis. The problem is that he gets very upset when most of the other horses go out and he becomes a nervous wreck. Any ideas?

A Having to restrict the grazing of a laminitis-susceptible horse is important, but, of course, creates problems in that it is difficult to tell the horse that being shut in the stable is for his own good!

Part of the problem for this particular horse is that he has an expectation about what normally happens in the morning, and finds it extremely difficult to be left in the stable whilst the other horses are leaving the yard. Weaving, door banging and box walking are behaviours that the horse will perform in his attempts to cope with a frustrating situation. In your case, the horse wants to escape from the box and follow his friends.

You could try leaving other horses in with him, but you must make sure that he can have proper interactions with them. In addition, if this is a fairly new experience for him it may be that, given time to adjust, his behaviour will settle down. However, it is important that he is protected from injury and that he does not suffer in his attempts to cope.

Get rid of pent-up energy

In order to help him learn to accept this new situation as normal, I suggest that you try to let the horse out as normal in the morning with the other horses, and allow him to 'let off steam', and then bring him in after a short while, say 15 to 30 minutes. It may be that he will more readily accept standing in, in the company of others, if he has had this chance to get rid of his pent-up energy. You can then distract him with an Equiball, or a turnip, or anything that will require him to work for small amounts of low quality food.

An alternative is to try taking him out for a ride first thing in the morning so that he cannot see the other horses being let out. Then you could feed him using an Equiball upon your return.

A new home

If these suggestions do not work and his behaviour continues, I strongly suggest that you should find him a yard where there is a starvation paddock or dirt yard where he can be in the company of other horses and ponies and his feed restricted without being restricted in all of his other activities.

Natalie Waran

Running away

"I GET THE FEELING MY HORSE COULD TAKE OFF AT ANY MOMENT!"

Q **My ex-trekking gelding has got into the habit of cantering down hills. This is very alarming as I have to ride down a very steep, narrow hill to get back to my stables. I currently ride him in a Dutch gag and a standing martingale, which does give me a bit more control, but I still get the feeling that he could take off at any moment.**

A Cantering downhill out of control can be a very frightening experience. You probably feel very unbalanced in this situation and that the

horse is able to use his weight against you far more than if you were going uphill. In reality, it is not half as dangerous as it feels. An ex-trekking pony will be very clever on his feet and sure of himself.

Regaining control
To begin with, do not canter down any hills at all, and do not canter on the way home, even when the going is flat. Keep rewarding him with

a pat and a kind word when he is walking sensibly without pulling.

Avoid hanging onto the contact when he hots up, but rather use half-halts followed by a lighter contact. You can only teach him to go on a lighter contact if he is able to experience a lighter contact, and this will only happen if he has responded to your aids to slow down. When you check him back, make sure you get some form of response to which you in turn are able to respond.

It would be inappropriate to use leg aids under these circumstances as this would confuse him as to whether he should be going faster or not. Even so, it is important that your legs remain in contact with his sides to keep him straight and to ride him forward quietly.

Relax

Talk to your horse all the time as this will have the added advantage of helping him to relax. Use the standard voice commands which he should already know from the ground, such as 'walk', 'whoa' and 'walk on!' Remember that he will respond to the tone of your voice just as much as the words you use, so keep your voice calm, firm and steady.

Your body language is important in as much as he will feel when you go rigid with anticipated fright, and then feel much more inclined to ignore you and take control himself. Try really hard to soften your muscles. This is best done by breathing correctly, especially breathing out. Even if all you can manage is a rapid blow, it is a start and will help to relieve tension. A confident and relaxed rider is more effective than one who senses danger all the time, and you need to talk yourself into being this confident and relaxed rider.

Transitions

Work on transitions in a straight line. This is best done going away from home when he will be less motivated to rush on. It is also a good idea to work in an open space so that you can circle should the need arise.

Aim to be able to put him into canter, in the open, and to bring him down to walk again, eventually without circling. When this is perfected on the flat, have a go downhill, again going away from home. Reward him constantly for good behaviour with a light contact, a pat and a kind word.

Aversion therapy

There is a wonderful cure for persistent cantering off downhill if you have access to open moorland or rolling, open hills - which few of us have. If the horse canters off down hill, let him go and push him up the next at the same speed.

Should he repeat his headlong rush down, you repeat the push up the next. Without any pulling or fighting, you then have a horse which associates rushing with having to labour uphill. It is very effective if you can do it!

You have a super, sensible, clever horse whose only fault is that he is wilful and has been poorly educated in the past. There is the challenging task of undoing his old habits before you will be able to do things in the way you choose. Rebuilding can be a very rewarding experience. You can do it!
Fliss Gillot

Careful clipping

"I'M HAVING A BATTLE GETTING MY YOUNGSTER USED TO CLIPPERS!"

Q **I'm having a real battle trying to get my youngster used to clippers and don't want to put him off for life! Could you explain the best way to approach this problem?**

A In general, there are two types of potentially difficult horses - those who have not yet experienced clipping, and those who have experienced it and have learnt to dislike it. For the first type, we need to look at habituating the horse to the clipping process, and shaping the horse's behaviour so that it responds in an unconcerned way when being clipped. And with the second type of horse, it must be desensitised to the process and relearn a new behavioural response.

For a horse who has not been clipped before, in a relaxed atmosphere - say, during feed times - the clippers should be switched on and left running for a while. Gradually, the motivation to feed, and the fact that nothing awful happens, ensure that the horse becomes habituated to the sound of the clippers nearby. Gradually, reduce the distance from the horse and, over time, combine grooming with the sound of clippers during feed times until eventually you can lay the clippers on the horse while they are vibrating. As the horse learns that the clippers are of no concern, the food is still there and nothing happens to him, clipping will be easy.

Horses that have already a learnt aversion to the clippers can be desensitised to them over time in much the same way. I suggest that the quiet battery kind of clipper is used, and that the horse is gradually introduced to hearing them nearby when feeding at the same time. If at any time the horse shows any anxiety, go back to the previous stage of the desensitisatioin programme, where the horse was unconcerned. Eventually, the horse may allow you to put the clippers on his body, while grooming him, and then lay them on while they are switched on.

The whole process will take a long time and require lots of patience. In some cases, horses are just too frightened to cope with the feel of the clippers and no amount of the softly-softly approach will help them - in which case, you have two options . . . Either keep him well-rugged early in the year and don't clip, or ask your vet to sedate him. He won't learn any new responses, but at least he won't be distressed and you will get the job done quickly and safely.
Natalie Waran

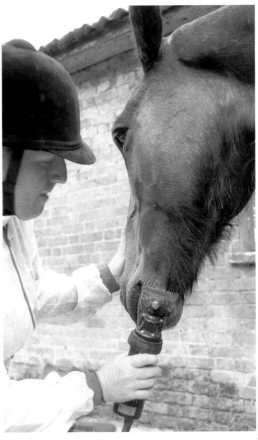

Referral dilemma

"DO I NEED A REFERRAL FROM MY VET?"

Q I'd like an osteopath to look at my horse, but do I need a referral from my vet?

A As the law stands, only veterinary surgeons are allowed to carry out acts of veterinary medicine. Strictly speaking, this means that osteopaths, massagers and acupuncturists are not acting within the law if they see cases on a first opinion basis. This can present a dilemma to the veterinary surgeon who, although may not wish to refer a horse for physiotherapy or osteopathy, is confronted by an owner insistent that the horse receives this treatment.

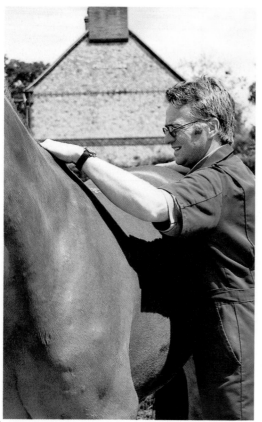

The vets come first
Physiotherapists and osteopaths are allowed to look at horses, but only under the direction of a veterinary surgeon. However, there are many unqualified and unskilled practitioners around who do go ahead and offer first-line advice and treatment.

If we want this situation rationalised, then we should really be reporting incidences of malpractice. But who is to do the reporting? It's unlikely to be the owner as it's his horse that is being treated. And as for the veterinary surgeon, he'd probably be accused of being churlish.

Protection for animals
Even in human medicine, there is not universal agreement over the abilities or effectiveness of osteopathic treatment. The human being is allowed to see an osteopath without first seeing a doctor because of the ability for self-referral. In other words, in man, it is considered that if people wish to take the risk of subjecting themselves to a therapy, that is their own prerogative.

The law, however, seeks to protect unwitting animals from abuse by introducing the mediation of the veterinary surgeon. This, though, has not really lead to the formation of co-operative links between veterinary surgeons, osteopaths and physiotherapists that it might have done.

You are probably right to be concerned at the lack of regulation in this field, but as far as the veterinary profession is concerned, there is little or nothing we can do about it. One has to look to the offices of the osteopaths and physiotherapists themselves if one wants to institute a more organised and rationalised system.
Rob Pilsworth

Planning permission

"I WANT TO BUILD STABLES ON MY LAND."

Q I would like to erect two stables on some land I own, which I bought originally as grazing land. Would I need planning permission to build these stables and also dog kennels and runs? I plan to live in a mobile home on the site.

A For the purpose of this reply, I assume that the established current use of the field is as agricultural land and that there are no existing planning consents for any other use. I also assume that there are no existing buildings or structures on the land.

Planning permission is ordinarily required for any 'development' carried out on land, and under Section 55 of the Town and Country Planning Act 1990 'development' is defined as 'building, engineering, mining or other operations in, on, over or under land or the making of any material change in the use of any building or other land."

The effect of this definition is that most building work or changes of use of land require planning permission, unless an exemption applies under the Town and Country Planning General Development Order or the (Use Classes) Order.

In the situation you describe, none of such exemptions would appear to apply and you will need planning permission to place a static caravan (or indeed any other caravan) on the land for the purposes of occupation.

Whilst planning permission is not required for the erection of stables and loose boxes within the grounds of a private dwelling house (subject to certain limitations as to size), the erection of stables on agricultural land will require planning permission. Similarly, the erection of kennels on agricultural land will require planning consent.

If the field in question is part of the Green Belt or situated in an Area of Outstanding Natural Beauty or an area registered as a Conservation Area, then stricter planning controls will apply than would ordinarily be the case, and it is unlikely that consent would be granted for these proposals.

However, you should consult your local planning authority as to their policy in the area and, subject to such information, you should seek the further advice of a planning consultant.
Richard Chamberlain

Hacking horror

"MY GELDING IS A NIGHTMARE TO HACK OUT."

Q **My 14-year-old gelding is a dream to show jump, cross country and school, but a total nightmare to hack out. He jogs, spins and rears and won't stand still to cross the road. He is fed on cool mix and a high fibre chaff, and ridden in a Dutch gag and running martingale.**

A The obvious conclusion is that your horse has been ridden at high speed whenever his feet have touched grass, which has had the effect of making him hyper-active. If there was anything seriously wrong with him, he would not be a dream to school, and he would certainly not be jumping well. This leads to the conclusion that the problem is psychological and that it should be possible, with time and patience, to school it out of him.

Initially, you need to find a situation that he can accept with calmness, such as walking quietly round his schooling paddock in the company of another horse. Even if all you have is an outdoor arena, you can still imagine that you are hacking by walking on long reins, chatting with your companion, and generally creating a very stress and pressure-free environment. Get someone to open the gate for you, if this is appropriate, and walk a short distance down the road.

Ride him forwards

Whenever possible, avoid turning round and walking home as this encourages napping. Work out a round route before you set out, very short to begin with. Whether it is once round the nearest housing estate, or round a triangle/island at the end of the road, going round anything reduces the feeling that your horse is allowed to turn round and go home. He must think forward all the time.

Keep your legs on his sides all the time, even if he boils up, so that he is thoroughly used to having to stay straight. Co-ordinate the use of your legs and hands to this end, so that you are able to keep him out of trouble as regards traffic and things at the side of the road. Have his head slightly turned into the traffic, so that he cannot swing his quarters to that side.

Work on getting him to stand still at a time when it doesn't matter to you whether or not he does stand. You are bound to get het up yourself if he is plungeing about in the path of an oncoming vehicle, and this will certainly make him worse. Praise him like mad (but quietly!) when he is good.

If you know there is a junction coming up, stop well back and always have someone with you who can stop the traffic if necessary, or at least tell you when it is safe to go forwards. In the meantime, walking in circles is better than rearing, so do this if it helps him to keep a grip on himself.

I hope you always wear a safety tabard saying 'Warning - Young Horse', even if he is 14 years old. Motorists are usually very understanding if they are warned that a horse is under training.

If he is highly strung, this horse would be better off being kept on a completely non-heating diet, which means avoiding all forms of grain. A calming supplement may help and is possibly worth a try, but I do feel that this is more of a schooling problem.

It is always worth getting his back checked if you haven't already done so. Sometimes skitting around like this causes all sorts of problems in the back area even if there was nothing wrong with the horse's back in the first place.

Fliss Gillott

Breaking fences

"I CAN'T KEEP MY MARE IN THE FIELD."

Q **I am desperately in need of help. My four-year-old cross-bred mare keeps escaping from her field. As soon as she is turned out and I have turned my back on her, she just breaks through the fence. The problem is only compounded by keeping her in, as she gets very het up, and can be unmanageable.**

A There are two ways of tackling this problem: one, why does she want to escape all the time, and two, how can you keep her in?

Why?
There are lots of reasons we could guess at. Perhaps she lacks stimulating company. Could it be that there is not enough to eat in her paddock? If she is getting cereals in her manger feed, it is possible that she is becoming almost hyperactive on the quickly-released energy from the cereal's starches.

How?
The fact that your horse can get out at all suggests that the fencing is inadequate. It may be fine for her companions, but not for this lively four-year-old. It is a matter of responsibility to ensure that fencing is up to the job.

If the fencing is wire, and she is squeezing through the strands, then it is not sufficiently tensioned. Wire strainers should be fitted, and then the wire made so tight that it is impossible to move it. A post and rail fence needs to have enough rails. They should be nailed to the inside of the posts, so that they acnnot be pushed off. Posts should be well dug in, concreted if necessary, so that they are strong. Any gaps in hedges should be railed up before there is an escape.

Electric fencing
All fencing is more secure for escapists if it is wholly or partially electrified. One or two strategically placed strands of electric wire will prevent a horse from pushing rails. Some or all of the strands of a plain wire fence can be replaced with electric. Hedges can be protected with a single or double row of electric wire or tape in front of them.

Electric fencing must be powered from a suitable energiser, not directly from the mains, or you will just electrocute the horse. There are available both mains operated and battery powered energisers. The wire or tape must be fixed using insulators, to prevent it shorting out. Very quickly, virtually all animals learn to respect electric fencing.

Keep it switched on all the time the horse is out, as they can be very quick to detect when the power is off. Some horses check the fence with their whiskers as soon as they are turned out, so it is not possible to fool them.

Temporary fencing
Many people use battery-powered fencing for their horse when away at competitions, especially endurance riders. They construct small paddocks for their horses rather than confine them to small or unsuitable stables. There are rarely any problems.

You will need two batteries (car type) and a mains battery charger, so you can be sure always of having a fully charged battery. You will need a battery powered energiser, electric tape (1cm width should do), of sufficient length to give two at least, or even three rows, and portable, push-in plastic stakes, enough for one every five metres or so. For the gateway, you will need stronger stakes and a sprung handle for each row of tape, with hooks to do them up to.

Once you can keep her in a paddock, she can have more time out of doors, which will probably make her happier and easier to handle.

Jane van Lennep

Wild when jumping

"MY ARAB MARE GOES WILD WHEN IT COMES TO JUMPING!"

Q I have an Arab mare who is fine to ride, except when it comes to jumping. She goes wild, spinning and bucking. What can I do as she is making me nervous?

A Horses which hot up in this manner when jumping are essentially lacking in basic schooling. With proper training in the beginning, being taught to maintain rhythm and balance

with poles on the ground, any horse will be able to learn to jump correctly.

This is not to deny that plenty of horses will become over-excited when jumping and still manage to jump successfully; the question is whether or not their exuberance is controllable and safe.

Jumping Arabs

Arabs are not always easy to teach to jump. The early stages may take much longer than with other types of horses, as their first reaction to anything new is to raise the head and consequently hollow the back. This is absolutely the reverse of what is required! Having said that, there are plenty of Arabs which have learnt to jump very well indeed and with great style and enthusiasm, but this is down to their trainers understanding their special needs and working with them, not against them. You will have to go right back to the beginning to sort out this mare's problems.

Unless she first learns to walk quietly over a pole on the ground, she will not improve. You may even have to lead her to start with, but be very careful not to get jumped on. Make sure you wear gloves and a hard hat. Be calm and patient whatever happens and reward her when she starts to make progress.

It is important to remember that Arabs have very sensitive mouths, even if they have a tendency to pull and hot up. Put this with a natural inclination to hollow and become head-high and it should be evident that you must not have any pressure on her mouth whatsoever while she is jumping. This is equally relevant for poles on the ground, where you are teaching your horse a pattern of behaviour that will be continued once the poles are raised.

An established jumping position

Unless you are in good balance, an awkward jump is going to leave you behind. You need a strategy to cope with this. Work on your jumping on an easier, more predictable horse; use a neckstrap or the mane to steady yourself; learn to slip your reins - all these techniques may prove of value.

You *must* free the mare's front end even if you are still trying to steady her on the approach. Give yourself a 'no-touch' zone a stride, or even two strides, before the obstacle and give your mare every chance to gain in confidence and develop her ability to round her back. Your position in the saddle is of importance as well, to avoid your weight coming down on her back just when she needs you to be light in the saddle.

Jumping exercises

Arrange your poles so that it is not easy for her to run out if she has a last minute panic. Place them against a safe fence to provide a guard on one side and then you can use spare poles to guard the other side.

Remember that loose poles can roll, so either have them raised above the height of the jump you are asking her to do or have them blocked by some means to prevent rolling. In a sand arena this is easy as you can scoop loose sand up on either side.

Only approach an obstacle when you have the mare under reasonable control and take time to relax her afterwards. Praise her when she does well, stay calm when she is over-excited. There may be days when you can only walk round the poles on the ground because the sight of them sends her into a spin. That is okay - after a few days of walking round the jumps and nothing happening, she will start to calm down sufficiently for you to make your first move.

Natural exuberance

Arabs tend to be exuberant jumpers and particularly brilliant cross-country. They rarely perform like machines under total rider control. Once an Arab has learnt *how* to jump, it is usually best allowed to get on with the job with little interference. The rider's task becomes that of pilot and advisor, giving the horse a correct approach line and suggested speed before letting the horse work out for itself how to clear the jump. Fortunately, they are quick and clever thinkers, able to see a stride and keep out of trouble.

A rider who interferes too much actually puts them off, which is why so many have the reputation for a tendency to throw in the odd stop. An Arab with the right rider is brilliant, but this is very definitely going to be an equal, co-operative partnership.

Fliss Gillott

Self-mutilation

"MY MARE BITES HER OWN LEGS."

Q **I recently bought an eight year-old Thoroughbred mare who has always been rather grumpy. Recently she has become vary bad tempered and I have noticed her banging her body against the wall and biting her legs. She only does this when she is stabled at night as she is fine in the paddock during the day.**

A It is very difficult given the limited information about how your horse is kept, and when your horse performs this bizarre behaviour, to say exactly why she is doing this.

This sort of behaviour is sometimes seen amongst stallions that are kept relatively isolated and confined for long periods of time. Self-mutilation often takes the form of flank biting and is thought to be a way of self stimulation caused by their need to cope with the unsuitable environment in which they are kept. Self-mutilation is more commonly seen in many animals kept in zoos, for example monkeys kept in barren cages have been observed to bite themselves.

I think the best thing for you to do is to firstly have a vet check her over to find out if there is any physical reason for her abnormal behaviour. It may be something simple, like a skin condition causing her to try to scratch herself by rubbing excessively on the walls of the stable, or it could be a symptom of some underlying painful condition.

Once you have eliminated any physical reason for the behaviour, I suggest that you try to find out from her previous owners if she exhibited this behaviour when she was with them. It may be that they can throw some light on the matter, perhaps giving you some insight into how she was kept there, and what may have caused the behaviour.

You will then need to try to keep a diary, noting down exactly when she performs the behaviour and if there are any triggers for it. She may, for example perform the behaviour only when you are around, which could suggest that she gets some reward from you by behaving as she does. Do you, for example, give her a lot of attention when she starts the behaviour, which may indicate that she has learned that by doing what she does, she receives attention, and this is rewarding for her. She may do it only before feeding, and is then rewarded by food.

In addition, you need to look at the way she is managed. It may be that, like the stallions I mentioned earlier, her behaviour is self-stimulating. This must lead you to consider whether her environment is adequate to meet her needs. You say that she is only housed at night, but you do not say whether she has contact with other horses during that time. She may be suffering from a lack of social contact with her own kind, and perhaps this could be easily solved by lowering the walls of the stable between her and a companion. Full partitions between horses do not give them the sort of social contact they need. A stable in which a horse spends up to 15 hours at night, alone and confined, is not a normal environment and can often lead to behavioural problems.

I think if the above prove to be of little use, it would be best to get in touch with an equine behaviour specialist. Ask your vet if he can refer you to someone in your area, who could come out and have a look at your horse and work with you both to try to solve the problem.
Natalie Waran

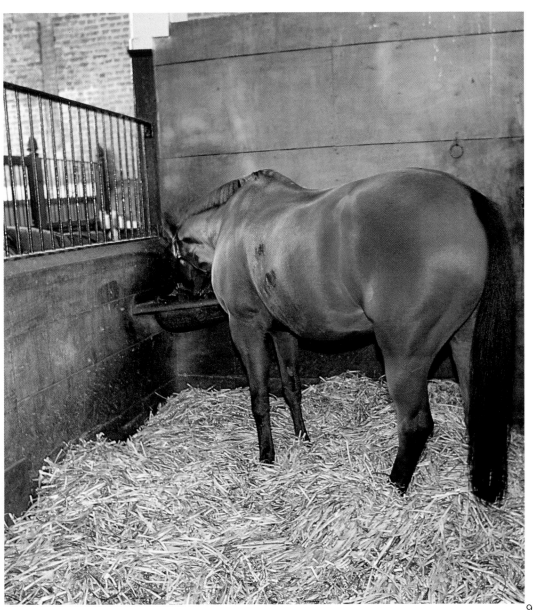

Active retirement

"HOW CAN I KEEP MY OUTGROWN PONY FIT?"

Q **I own a 13hh mare which I have sadly outgrown. I can't bear to put her out on loan, but I need to keep her fit. I don't have the money to buy a harness to drive her, so how can I prevent her getting fat and unfit?**

A It is always sad when you find you have outgrown a favourite pony which feels more like a friend than an animal, and I can fully sympathise with your wanting to keep her.

Too many people are happy to sell ponies on when they are well past their prime and settled in familiar surroundings. If the ideal home can be found, then this is fine, but you are clearly not prepared to take this chance.

It is a pity you have not mentioned your approximate height and weight, or the type of the pony. Some ponies are capable of carrying much greater weights than would normally be expected, as long as the rider is well balanced and sympathetic to the pony's needs.

The other important factor is that the saddle is a comfortable fit for both pony and rider. You cannot fit an adult-sized bottom into a child-sized saddle as the weight then becomes too concentrated for both parties. It is always important that a saddle gives a comfortable fit over the withers as well as along the back but especially so when the rider is on the large side.

I cannot give you a guide as to a maximum weight for a 13hh pony to carry, as there are so many variables to take into account. What I will say, though, is keep an open mind to this possibility. 15 to 20 minutes of the right sort of work several times a week will be more than enough to keep your little mare happy and moderately fit, even if jumping is out of the question.

Alternatives to riding

Long reining is an alternative to riding if you feel she needs the stimulation of going out and about round the countryside. You could use two lunge reins, or long cords known as plough lines. These are not easy to get hold of as few horses work on the land, but you can buy the right sort of lightweight rope from sailing shops and make your own.

It is important that they are not too heavy or rough in case they get pulled through your hands (always wear gloves) or caught round the pony's legs. The advantage of cord is that it does not blow about on windy days!

Have a go in a safe environment if you have never long reined before, at least until you have mastered the art of coping with two very long reins! It is advisable only to go out in company until you are very competent and confident, especially on the roads. Ideally, have somebody walking by her head to give her a lead should it prove necessary. Once you are ready to go, you will both become very fit indeed and could go for hours at a time.

A final option is to ride and lead if you have the use of another horse. Again it is essential to master the art before you go near a road, but both led horse and ridden horse are able to get a lot of pleasure from the company in this situation.

I hope this gives you some ideas which will help you to get the most from your pony and to provide her with an active and healthy retirement.
Fliss Gillott

Change of character

"MY MARE HAS SUDDENLY BECOME VIOLENT TOWARDS OTHER HORSES."

Q Up until recently my mare had been very happy at her yard. She is turned out regularly and has contact with a mixed herd.

However, she has started to get very violent towards a new Clydesdale gelding in the adjacent stable. She squeals and kicks at the walls and is particularly bad at feeding times. She now reacts in the same way to any horse close to her.

A It seems fairly clear that your mare was quite content prior to the arrival of a particular horse that has provoked her to behave in a protective way over her food and, it seems her space.

Although it may seem odd that she has taken exception to this particular horse, and has since then generalised her response to other horses housed next to her, it's not that unusual, when you consider the environment that horses have evolved to live in.

An unnatural environment

Horses in their natural environment are not forced to defend their space or food, since these resources are usually plentiful and in the case of grass, evenly spread.

In the domestic environment, horses are expected to feel at ease in a stable, next to others they have often had no free time interacting with, and eating concentrated food from a bucket. Mostly horses cope well with this regime, but when there are problems it is because an individual is pushed too far.

In your case your mare felt threatened by the Clydesdale gelding, who probably invaded her flight zone, and being in the stable, she was unable to put the distance she wanted to between them.

Being unable to control the environment often leads to anxiety and stress. I would suggest that this is why she has generalised her behaviour to all horses next to her in the stable. She is determined to try to take control of what seems to her a threatening situation. It also explains why she is happy to stand near horses when she is turned out in the field, for here she can move away if she wants to, so she feels more comfortable.

Stress-free feeding

I suggest that the best way to her now, is to feed her in a stable with no one either side of her, or with plenty of room so that she feels less threatened. You will probably find that once she no longer feels she has to protect her food from those housed next to her, she no longer responds to them at other times.

In addition, you may like to feed her using a food ball, so that her feeding time is longer, and feeding is a little less frantic. Although you are not actually curing her protective aggression, sometimes managing it is actually less traumatic and more successful.

I also suggest that you check to make sure that there are no clinical explanations that may explain her increased feeding motivation. She may have an inefficient digestion perhaps due to worms, problems with teeth, or something more complicated.

I hope that these suggestions help you to understand and manage her problems, so that she can enjoy her stabled life again.
Natalie Waran

DIY rights

"WHAT RIGHTS DO I HAVE AT MY DIY YARD?"

Q **I keep my horse at a DIY livery yard, where terms were verbally agreed in good faith. But now things are changing and certain facilities are off limits. Do I have any rights?**

A Unfortunately, livery yards are not regulated in the same way as licensed riding schools and the riding Establishments Act 1970 only applies to riding schools offering lessons to the general public.

Even if the Act did apply, the problems you have encountered would not be subject to statutory control. Your problem is that the livery yard owner has 'moved the goalposts' and is now refusing to allow you to use facilities which you had previously agreed would be provided. This is simply a matter of contract law. Unless the variation was agreed, the livery yard owner will be in breach of contract.

Nevertheless, the law does not require that such an agreement must be in writing and the mere absence of a written agreement does not affect the contractual liability of both parties.

Your biggest problem . . .

In your case, however, your verbal agreement does not appear to have covered the question of termination and what was to happen in the event of either side breaking the agreement. Therefore, the biggest problem you face is that the yard owner's breach of contract only gives you a momentary right to compensation. By leaving your horse at the yard, you may be deemed to have accepted the new terms imposed by the yard owner at the same cost, thereby giving rise to a new contract.

Even if you had had a written contract with the yard owner, it would still have been open to the yard owner to seek to change the terms of the agreement, unless it was specifically recorded that the agreement was to run for a fixed period – during which the terms could not be altered by either side without the agreement of the other.

If the yard owner will not restore your use of the facilities, then the only sensible course is to find an alternative yard. However, it is always wise to secure a written agreement when placing a horse at livery. Such agreement should include terms dealing with. . .

● the facilities that will be provided
● turnout arrangements
● insurance
● security arrangements
● how long the agreement is to run for
● the basis on which it might be terminated within that period
● the amount of care and any other services to be provided by the yard owner
● the cost.

Richard Chamberlain

Can't catch me!

"WHAT COULD HAVE CHANGED MY HORSE?"

Q **Muffin used to be a popular riding school horse, but when she was turned into a livery, her character started to change. She unceremoniously dumped her new owner and within three months she was back at the riding school. I have since bought her, but now she refuses to be caught in the field – not even with some feed. We have had experts in to try Join Up – unsuccessfully – and even though she's a handful, she has never been aggressive and my son loves her. What can you advise?**

A It is difficult to get 'inside' Muffin's head without seeing her in person and the expression on her face when she refuses to be caught. She is clearly a very confused and unhappy horse, having suffered so many changes in what must be a relatively short space of time. Her confidence has been shattered and continues to be damaged with every new trauma which, although of her own making, is not through her choice.

Distrusts your motives
Riding school ponies are often perceived to have a hard life but they are able to enjoy regular work, a fixed routine and constant companionship of other horses and ponies. This must have suited Muffin and yet she lost it. What happened, I wonder, when she was away for three months with the man who had fallen off her?

It would seem that even since you bought this mare, she has had reason to distrust your motives for catching her. Incidentally, I have observed over the years that the most sensitive and 'aware' mares are sometimes prone to being difficult to catch, but are fantastic with small children even when they trust no-one else. The fact that Muffin has never shown any aggression would suggest that she may have this particular trait.

Somehow, you need to convince her that you and your family are to be trusted and will be good company when she is ready to join you.

Breaking the pattern
Your family could spend some time with Muffin when the weather is reasonable, so why not take a picnic out to her field when she is out alone? Take the dog if you have one and let it play in the field, as long as it doesn't chase Muffin!

Ideally, if there is not much grass, the space is limited and Muffin is alone, you will have a much better chance of rousing her curiosity.

If she comes to you, ignore her and make no attempt to catch her. Leave a juicy apple where she could pick it up without being touched.

Maybe your son could approach her with a tasty morsel but clearly, you will have to be as certain that he won't get kicked. The point is that until Muffin wants to come to you, the battle will continue.

Somehow you have to break that pattern of mistrust and let her feel that being with you is a positive experience and not a prelude to something potentially frightening (in her mind) or unpleasant.

Are you patient enough to visit her every day and attend to her needs whilst putting any ideas of working her, shoeing her or having her vaccinated to the back of your mind until things improve?

Build a routine
There is lots for Muffin to overcome before you can make any progress. It is easier to learn from scratch than it is to unlearn and then relearn.

On a more positive note, Muffin did have an apparently long spell when she was happy and content with her lot in life. This means that her trust in people has a hope of being rekindled.

If you cannot catch her, chasing her will make

her worse. But putting a feed out for her at the same time each day will start to rebuild her routine. Use a hook-on manger and wait on the other side of the fence for her to come over. Make a fuss of her through the fence while she enjoys her feed. Then you may be able to do this from her side of the fence without trying to catch her.

Don't try to catch her until you can move all round her while she is eating and run your hands over her neck, shoulders and back. When you do catch her, make it a positive experience so that she starts to look forward to your visits instead of dreading them.

Uphill task
As long as she is not clipped, Muffin will be fine without a rug on. Leaving her feet untended will be less harmful if she has no shoes and she will probably be fine without a 'flu jab if she is not going to horse shows.

You have an uphill task with no guarantee of success at the end of it, but you stand to gain so much with Muffin if you have the patience to see it through. Good luck!
Fliss Gillott

When to wean

"WHEN SHOULD I WEAN MY COLT - AND HAVE HIM GELDED?"

Q **I have recently purchased a five-month-old cob colt and his mother. I would like advice on weaning, which is imminent, and at what age he should be gelded as he is showing 'coltish' behaviour.**

A I would urge you to wait before weaning your colt as it is an important part of his nutrition. The young horse's gut is not sufficiently well developed to cope with a mainly fibrous diet until seven-and-a-half months, so that alone would suggest that weaning should not take place until then. Natural weaning occurs much later.

Stress-free weaning

An abrupt, early weaning is psychologically damaging to the foal. People are only just beginning to realise the full impact of this on the foal, having taken for granted the fact that foals will always call for days when weaned, always lose weight and have to be shut in a dark stable with the top door shut to prevent injuries when they try to escape.

The mare will also be upset, calling frantically for her foal and continuing to make milk for it. A later, more gradual weaning will result in less or even no stress, and none of

the aspects of weaning so many folk have taken for granted.

When to cut

Next, let's look at castration. The earlier this is done, the better. If you can do it while the foal is still on the mare, so much the better. He can go to her for warm milk and comfort when he comes round and will be far less traumatised.

Early cutting, before coltish behaviour has become established, means the youngster is much easier to handle. Testosterone has a lot to answer for! It also creates a feeling of euphoria. Late castration means that the horse has been living with his testosterone for longer and, when it abruptly ceases, will feel depressed.

Gelding and growth

The sex hormones also play a part in the closing of the growth plates of the bones. Early castration, to many people's surprise, actually results in bigger adults because they will grow for longer. I breed Arabs and have twice had clear evidence of this. A colt whose father was very special was left entire until he was four, but as his sire was still very fit and alive and another stallion was not needed, he was gelded. He made just 15hh. His full brother was gelded as a foal, before weaning. He is a good 15.3hh.

The same situation repeated itself several years later with another stallion and a different mare. The horse gelded at five years made under 14.2hh. His full brother, gelded at 10 months, is over 15hh as a three-year-old and still growing. As your chap is already feeling coltish, I think it is time to book the vet before he causes any trouble.

There is a long road ahead of you if you stick with your plans to bring on this young pony. It will be hard at times, frustrating when things go less than well, but immensely rewarding when things do go according to plan. There are many people in your situation, and most of them in the end reckon it was worth it!

Jane van Lennep

Sarcoids

"ARE THEY SARCOIDS?"

Q **My horse has recently developed some flat, crusty, wart-like nodules. What are they and how can I prevent them spreading? I notice he has recently developed something similar on his nose.**

A These lesions sound like sarcoids, although the more recent growths on the nose may be warts and unrelated to the flat, crusty areas on the neck. Warts, papillomas and sarcoids are often used non-specifically to describe skin lesions, even though each cell structure is different, as is the potential for invasive growth.

Still not enough is known about the exact cause of such skin lesions, with theories ranging from a yet unclassified virus to a form of skin cancer. This makes their treatment rather hit-and-miss, because very few biopsies are taken to confirm the exact nature of the lesions. The lesions can be treated aggressively using chemotherapy, which has to be administered by your veterinary surgeon due to the toxic nature of the chemical involved. There is often substantial erosion of the surrounding tissue which can cause the horse pain until the flesh has fully healed.

There has, however, also been some success with homeopathic remedies which are best given as internal medication. These remedies include Thuja, Carcinosin and Causticum. Alternatively, a small sample of sarcoid or wart tissue can be sent to a homoeopathic pharmacy who will prepare a nosode. Given, for example, on a regular basis, the nosode 'alerts' the body to dealing with a problem in its own tissue. Depending on the origin of the lesion, the close match of tissue remedy can stimulate the horse's body to gradually replace the diseased cells of the sarcoid with healthy ones.

It has been suggested that the appearance of sarcoids is linked to vaccinations or herpes infections. Again, specific homeopathic nosodes or vaccines may halt the sarcoid development. And creams containing vitamin E or Aloe Vera may reduce skin lesions, but it is not always known whether or not these are really sarcoids.
Sara Wyche

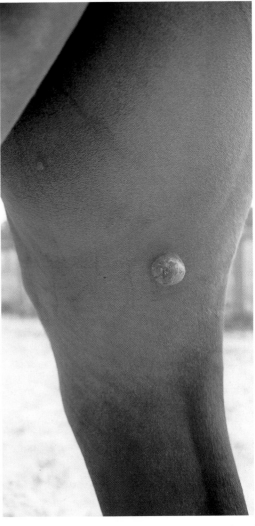

Vocalisation

"SHE WON'T STOP WHINNYING!"

Q **My new mare has a habit of whinnying loudly at other horses whilst out hacking. She will even whinny at passers-by when I school her**

A It always takes time for horses to settle into new surroundings, and for them to feel secure. I feel that your horse lacks confidence and she will gradually build her confidence as she becomes used to dealing with new horses, situations and people.

The language of the horse is a subtle one. As with most animals, they rely much more on body language than do humans. Although vocalisations do appear to confer some information, they are perhaps less specific and more limited. This is probably because horses living in herds are rarely out of sight of each other, and so can make use of visual signals.

Horse vocalisation

There appear to be four basic types of horse vocalisation: the nicker, the whinny (or neigh), the squeal and the groan. All of these have been recorded from horses in a variety of situation.

The nicker is a low-pitched pulsating sound, about 100Hz, and is formed with the mouth shut. It is usually used as a greeting for maintaining contact, especially between dam and young, and in anticipation of a pleasurable event, such as feeding.

The whinny is usually fairly loud, up to 2000Hz. It appears to be used in a wide variety of circumstances, ranging from social isolation to aggressive threats, and so may be thought of as a means of establishing contact.

The squeal is generally associated with aggressive or threatening encounters with other horses. It appears to act as a warning signal to ward off unwelcome attention.

The groan is used by horses in anguish or discomfort, such as a mare struggling to deliver a foal. Other sounds made by the horse are non-laryngeal, that is they are not produced using the larynx. Of these, the snort appears in conflict situations, but also when the horse is clearing its airways, and when it encounters an interesting odour.

The snort of the herd stallion often appears to act like an alarm call, attracting the attention of the members of the herd. The blow seems to indicate high arousal, when the horse is in a state of anxiety and it can carry up to 200 metres. This appears to have similar characteristics to the bark of an anxious dog.

It seems most likely that the horse's vocalisations serve to *attract attention* and to relay information about the general state of arousal, than as a means of transmitting specific information. The context of the sounds and the visual signals given by the producer are probably used by the receiver in interpreting the more specific meaning of the communication. Therefore, it is likely that your mare is attempting to maintain contact with the horses in her new home, and I am certain that over time, as she gains more confidence, she will need to do this less and less.

You should try to introduce her to different situations and places, at first in the presence of a familiar horse, and, as she gains in confidence and acceptance of novel situations, she can start to face things alone. You need patience and tact and eventually she will learn to cope with life at her new home.
Natalie Waran

Lazy horse

"MY EX-RIDING SCHOOL COB IS RELUCTANT TO WORK."

Q I am loaning a 14.2hh native x cob from my riding school. He is six years old and a bit green. He is very lazy and reluctant to work, especially in the school, and he dislikes hacking out on his own. He also has a habit of kicking other horses, especially mares.

A It is a difficult transition for a horse to make, from riding school work to schooling or hacking as an individual. This horse sounds very lazy and is not afraid to have and express his own opinions. Kicking mares appears, on the face of it, to be aggressive behaviour, although sometimes kicking can be a sign of nervousness and self defence. Either way, both his laziness and his bad behaviour need to be overcome through strong and confident riding and management.

Health checks

It is always advisable to have a horse's health checked out if he is persistently lacking in energy and seems dull and listless. You could talk to your vet about this, as a blood test may be necessary to check that he is not lacking in any way. Is he regularly wormed and does he look well covered? Is his coat glossy and his skin supple?

It must be said that if a horse is fit and healthy, but still prone to laziness, then 'corning him up' will not make him any more willing. Very often it has the reverse effect, making them more energetic in the determination not to co-operate. However, an adequate diet is essential even for horses in light work. I cannot help thinking that a lot of this horse's behaviour is due to him feeling out of sorts, as well as 'green' and insecure.

Ridden work

Once his general health is sorted out, you will be able to devote some time to his other problems. He has probably had enough of working in the school for the time being, so take him out as much as you can, in the company of other horses. This will be more fun for both of you, and will help to build up a partnership between you and him.

Encourage him to start taking a lead as often as you can, starting with him just having his nose in front. Avoid nagging constantly with your legs, but encourage him to listen to your legs and maintain his rate of progress until you ask him to do something else. It is better to reinforce your leg aids with a sharp kick or a quick flick with a schooling whip than to deaden his sides. Always praise him when he tries for you, and gauge your work to improve his fitness but not to wear him down.

Warn other people to keep away from your horse's back end. Then, if you teach him to go forward and straight, he will be unable to kick. This is one of the few 'crimes' for which a horse should be punished, but only if you react immediately and spontaneously. If you cannot do this, hitting him will only cause further hurt and confusion. To this end, carry a schooling whip so that there is not delay while you take your hand off the reins and use your stick.

Kicking is potentially very dangerous - I know of several people who have suffered broken legs or ankles having been kicked by another horse while they have been riding themselves. If he is shod behind, you should seriously consider having his hind shoes taken off to reduce the risk of serious injury. This need not prevent you from hacking out just as much as you do now.

Hind feet take much less wear than than front feet and will harden in response to the wear they endure. It is customary to put a red ribbon on the tail of a known kicker, so you should consider doing this when you ride in company.

Remember that you are the boss. If you tell your horse to do something, either from the ground or from the saddle, he should do it. As he learns to respect you, he will become a more willing ride and will actually gain confidence as well as obedience. This is necessary before you can really relax and become good friends as well as partners. Praise him when he is good and let him know when he is bad.

Avoid asking too much of him, especially if you do not feel up to it for any reason, but do not be afraid to push when the time is right. You obviously both need time and will both need help occasionally, so ask for it when you need it. By the time the weather improves, you should be ready to get out and enjoy yourselves together.
Fliss Gillott

Manners maketh horse

"MY MARE HAS TERRIBLE MANNERS."

Q My 10-year-old mare naps, rears, bucks and is unfriendly to other horses. Plus, she doesn't load very well and needs to be led with a chain. I've tried to lunge her, but she just charges at me and actually pushes me over - although she is well-behaved at shows. I'm a competent rider and am studying horses at college - plus my instructor is helping me a great deal - but I'm not sure what to do next. Can you advise me please?

A As a 10-year-old, your mare has come to you with some behavioural baggage, which includes being difficult to manage when you're on the ground. It is interesting that she is less inclined to misbehave when she's in an unfamiliar place, such as at a show. This suggests she's a bright mare, who has worked out how she can get her own way at home, but isn't so sure when she's in a strange place.

I'm glad to hear that your instructor is helping you and that you're taking a course in horse management. All of this should help you to understand why your mare is behaving so inappropriately. First, ask your vet to make sure she is healthy and that there is no physical problem underlying her reluctance to be with other horses, load or be lunged. Some mares show extreme behavioural responses during oestrus and this sort of behaviour can be managed with drugs.

Keep a diary
Once you've established that she is healthy, begin a diary to extablish exactly what situations cause your mare problems. In addition, you should - with your instructor - teach her the correct responses from the ground. This will require that you have control over her in a small arena, with a bridle on and a lunge rope attached, and a strong and experienced person holding her. She should be taught to move forwards, backwards, sideways, and to halt and stand, all for a food reward and praise. You should be firm with her if she attempts to push on you.

You may wish to spend time playing the games that are described by Pat Parelli or using the techniques of body language discribed by Monty Roberts and Kelly Marks. Any of these methods will encourage you to spend time working out why your horse uses her strength against you. Your aim is to establish that you are in charge, you have her trust, and that she wants to work with you rather than against you!

If all this seems too daunting and you are worried for your safety, you may wish to consider selling or loaning your mare to a more experienced person, who may be better suited to her.

Natalie Waran

Rescue case

"I'M THINKING OF RESCUING SOME FOALS..."

Q **I am thinking about rescuing two or three New Forest foals from the sales and training them up to be children's riding ponies.**

A Although it is very admirable that you are planning to give these ponies a better deal, I think there are a lot of points which need to be considered before you actually go ahead.

First of all, by buying these ponies, even at the very low prices they usually fetch, you are creating more demand for them at the sales, which will have the effect of encouraging more breeding. An awful lot of the problems seen with these ponies is because there are just too many of them being bred in the Forest, and measures to reduce breeding would probably do more for

their welfare than anything which might encourage further breeding.

Suitable mounts?
I think it is pertinent to look at the future suitability of these ponies as children's mounts. Whilst very many New Forests are undoubtedly excellent children's ponies, it is also true to say that there are also those which do not make the grade. New Forests are not quick to mature, and at four years old will not normally be ready for a child to ride. It has to be said, that until they settle down as they get older they can very often pack a mean buck!

Would you buy one?

Put yourself in the position of a concerned parent buying a pony for their child. Would you make your first choice a pony which had been totally wild until it was put through a sale ring at the same time as it was separated from its mother, and underwent its first journey? It is very traumatic, and such experiences can damage a pony's mental health.

In trying to get wild ponies handled, and confident, it is very hard to avoid the shy, timid creature, becoming a spoilt monster overnight, as its confidence in you grows. It will be a long time before a pony from such a situation will be a reliable, saleable child's pony, bearing in mind that these are intelligent, late-maturing ponies with the worst possible start in life.

Some important considerations

Should you decide to go ahead with this project, you will need lots of time and money, not to mention patience and good, pony-proof fences! If they are in poor condition and badly pulled down by worms, you also must accept the possibility that they may not make it, or that having survived physically, they do not have the right temperament. You must be prepared to make some very big decisions on their behalf.

Transporting wild ponies can be undertaken in a lorry or trailer, but make sure it is totally secure and that the trailer's back doors are done up so there is no chance of them trying to escape. You will have to travel them loose, as they will not even have been halter broken. Take out all the partitions and make sure there is nothing on which they could injure themselves. Ensure that grooms' doors cannot possibly be opened from the inside, and make sure that there is some way you can check them without having to open a door or go in with them. In their terrified state, any opening could be seen as an escape route.

Keep them with an older, steady pony who can set them a good example of manners, and demonstrate that you are not to be feared. At first keep them together in a large stable or small barn, until they have got used to you and will approach you when you bring their food. Then they can go in a small paddock, but come in for feeding and so you can start to handle them and put on headcollars, for instance.

A vet should check them out for you and can give you advice on worming and innoculations. If they are in very poor condition, they may not even be able to take worming, and certainly will not be strong enough to be vaccinated. You will need to build them up a bit first.

Feeding is best kept to good quality forages. Good, soft meadow hay should be available all the time. Base your short feeds on soaked sugar beet, with some alfalfa pellets added. I also like seaweed as an extra food for native ponies, perhaps with some linseed.

Do not undertake this project lightly. It is a minefield, even for people with a lot of experience with youngsters. I have spoken to people who have done what you are planning, and their advice would be 'don't!' The reality is far from the dream of wild ponies becoming tame, friendly and then perfect. Going to the sales is likely to break your heart, and that is only the beginning.

Jane van Lennep

Wobbler syndrome

"I NEED INFORMATION"

Q I have a two-year-old colt who has been diagnosed as suffering from 'Wobbler syndrome'. He is well in himself, but his co-ordination has gone in his hind legs. He has received a steroid injection, but I would appreciate any further information or advice on treatment.

A Wobbler syndrome in horses is usually produced by physical pressure on the nerves of the spinal cord of the neck. Because of the anatomy of the spinal cord, the nerves from the hind legs are those placed lowest in the spinal cord as it runs up the neck. If these nerves are physically compressed, they stop working, just as sitting on a hard object for a period of time can have the same effect on the sciatic nerve in the leg, giving the 'dead leg/pins and needles' syndrome in humans.

The causes

The pressure producing the lesion in cases of wobbler syndrome comes from an abnormality in the neck. This can be a physical angle change in the bones of the neck at one joint, which is called subluxation. Alternatively, the pressure can come because of the development of early onset arthritis in the joints of the neck. This produces new bone around the joint making the joint larger than normal. These 'knuckles' of new bone press on the nerve cord as the horse lowers its head and produce the lack of sensation in the back legs, which is seen as inco-ordination (ataxia).

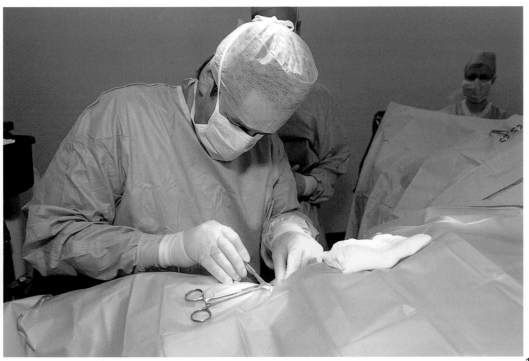

The influence of OCD

For many years, it was known that there was a hereditary component to the development of wobblers, but no-one was quite sure why. An experimental breeding programme in America mated a male wobbler stallion with females similarly affected. The expected outcome was that the offspring would have a massive preponderance of cases of wobbler disease.

Unexpectedly, this did not occur, but what did happen was that almost 80% of the offspring were affected with a cartilage development condition called osteochondrosis dissecans (OCD). OCD is a relatively common condition in rapidly growing horses, most commonly the Standardbred and Thoroughbred.

It is now thought that many cases of wobbler disease are in fact the result of osteochondritic lesions in the neck and it is these primary lesions which lead to the development of arthritis, and subsequent nerve cord compression.

Surgical treatment

Once the arthritic changes are present around the neck joints, there is no way to remove the new bone and, therefore, the spinal cord will continue to be compressed when the horse raises and lowers its head. One solution that may be worth considering is a surgical intervention, which produces stiffening in the neck to prevent the movement which causes the excessive pressure.

This is called 'basket' surgery. It involves drilling out a plug-shaped hole across the bottom of the joints exerting compression on the spinal cord. Once the cork-shaped piece of bone is removed, a metal basket of the same size and shape is tapped in. This produces a restriction on the degree of flexion produced when the horse raises and lowers its head. Usually this results in an improvement in the degree of ataxia without a total cure.

Prior to surgery, the surgeon will invariably X-ray the neck and may do a contrast study, called a myelogram, where radio opaque dye is injected around the spinal cord to confirm the site of compression. This dye can be seen being pinched off at the sites of compression, and will appear like a string of sausages where it becomes pinched in by the compression from the bones of the neck.

Whether or not your horse would be a candidate for this surgery will be largely dependent on the initial degree of ataxia. Most surgeons grade ataxia, on a scale of one to five, and they expect an improvement of approximately one to two grades following basket surgery. If your horse is now a grade five ataxia, then even surgical intervention is still going to leave him so inco-ordinated as to be a danger to himself and others.

My advice would be to discuss with your veterinary surgeon the possibility of referral to a specialist surgeon experienced in the technique of basket placement.

Rob Pilsworth

Schooling on a hack

"ARE THERE ANY SCHOOLING EXERCISES I CAN DO WHILST HACKING?"

Q **I have a young horse who needs to progress in his schooling. The problem is I don't have a school and my fields are often too wet to ride on. Are there any schooling exercises I can do whilst out hacking?**

A Schooling out hacking is a wonderful way to augment schooling at home all year round, as well being a very valid method of schooling when there are no other options available. Without going into minute details about how to perform individual exercises, I can give you a list of things to try, either on the road or along tracks.

Ride forward and straight

You should do this anyway, but it will be helpful on the road to prevent shying and will make sure your horse remains active and balanced. It is not necessary to have the horse 'on the bit' all the time, although sometimes this will be the case.

The horse may be on a long rein, or even a loose rein, and should still be forward and straight. If you find you have to use your legs constantly, then this is another area to work on - answering the leg so that you are both free to enjoy a relaxing ride.

Lengthening and shortening the stride

This can be done in walk, trot or canter. If you are not sure about the feel you should be getting, then work on going faster or slower within the gait without the horse trying to change gait.

The horse should maintain a steady rhythm. If you are careful not to allow the horse to quicken his steps when you send him forward, you will be on the way to developing longer or shorter steps on command.

Practise transitions

A good transition is smooth, balanced and

unhurried, but should happen at the moment it is required. Quick off the leg, light in the hand, a good transition will work the horse well by encouraging him to use his hindquarters and limbs efficiently.

Set yourself markers using trees or fence posts for instance, to improve your accuracy and the horse's obedience to the aids. Even halting at a road junction is an opportunity to work on a straight transition in and out of a square halt, with the horse quietly on the bit. It is much safer than jigging around in the traffic as well!

Leg yielding and shoulder-in

Lateral work can be practised anywhere. Shoulder-in is particularly useful with a horse that is likely to shy as it will keep it nicely to the aids and out of trouble. Shoulder-in may be used to correct just about any problem that may arise.

For example, if your horse jogs on the way home, a few steps of shoulder-in will encourage more attention to the rider and less to getting back to the stable. Use it again if you have had trouble getting the horse to the aids again after a brisk canter. The possibilities are endless.

Circles and bends

If space permits, it is sometimes possible to put in an occasional circle of maybe six to 10 metres. If you do this (in walk), try to decide in advance what size circle you intend to ride and test your ability to ride accurately.

Spending too much time doing little circles down the bridlepath, however, will eventually lose you the advantage of the free forward movement which hacking out encourages so well.

From a straight line, ask your horse to bend a little to one side before straightening and then bending equally to the other side. This should be done while the horse is on the bit, and followed by stretching the neck forward and down. This, in turn, will stretch the whole topline encouraging the horse to remain supple through his body.

Making progress

Make sure your horse is worked in before you ask too many questions. Allow plenty of time to unwind and enjoy just being out and about. As long as your horse will come to the aids without an argument, there is no need to work him too much to the hand. If you overschool, he will end up being jaded and resistant.

By doing a certain amount of schooling out hacking, and by making sure that your horse is ready to come together when you ask him to, you should find that schooling progresses much more quickly than if you were restricted to an arena.

Schooling on a hack also has the benefit of avoiding double standards whereby the horse is allowed to slop around when he is out, but is not allowed the same laxity in the arena!

Fliss Gillott

Loves to lick

"MY MARE LICKS ALL SORTS OF THINGS."

Q My 11-year-old mare loves to lick. She will lick all sorts of things from people to the walls of her wooden stable and fence posts. Do you have any explanation for this strange behaviour?

A Licking can be a disconcerting habit, or an endearing one, depending on your point of view! I do not believe there is any definitive answer as to why some horses lick more than others.

One possibility is that your mare is looking for salt. Salt licks should always be available to horses. You can use a plain or a mineralised one - flavoured ones are also available. Personally, I use the mineralised licks. They are the size and shape of a house brick and can either be left in the manger, where they also prevent the horse from bolting its food, or they can be fixed in a holder to the fence or the stable wall.

The horse can help itself to the salt as and when it feels the need. Some horses use their licks a lot, others never touch them. Sometimes, if they have been without a lick for a while, they will devour a whole lick in a day or so, but if you replace it, you should find that they soon settle down. My herd of 10 horses gets through one lick every two to four weeks in the field.

I have also known horses lick after eating something strongly flavoured, such as mints. It is as if the flavour is too strong and they are trying to get it off their tongue. Maybe there is something you are feeding your mare which she finds has a strong taste?

You may have to accept that this is something your horse does, with no logical explanation. It could simply be a quirk of her nature.

Jane van Lennep

Too old to learn

"OLD DOG - NEW TRICKS!"

Q I have recently taken on a 13-year-old horse with only limited schooling. He can sometimes be a bit of a handful, although I do lunge him before I ride to take the 'sting' out of him. Am I wasting my time in trying to improve his way of going or is it possible to teach an 'old dog' new tricks?

A Your horse is anything but too old to learn to work properly. It may take a little longer than with a younger horse, but this is because he has to do some 'unlearning' before he can start learning. Although you could argue that, as he has never been schooled before, he has not learnt any bad habits, but he has still been allowed to please himself and will expect this state of affairs to continue.

Keep it simple

You need to keep his early lessons simple and make sure your horse remains focused on being forward, straight and obedient. You are right to try and 'tame' his high spirits before you ask him to listen and work. He would find it very difficult to concentrate at the moment without this sympathetic gesture on your part, although in time this energy should become 'free' impulsion!

A suitable routine

Try to avoid over-schooling. Two to three days a week should be more than enough, especially if you carry his lessons forward into hacking. Although it would be unkind and probably pretty difficult to keep him 'on the bit' at all times, obedience to the aids and general good manners should be constant. Otherwise, he will need periods when he can relax, unwind and simply enjoy being ridden as he was able to before his schooling became important.

He will need to build his confidence so that as time goes by, he can cope with the same amount of work as any other horse of his age.

By aiming to channel his exuberance rather than supress it, and keeping his work varied and interesting, there is no reason for this horse not to thrive in his new role. Horses are like people as they age - keep them active and learning, and they will continue to be active and capable of picking up new tricks. So have a good time!
Fliss Gillott

Mean what you say!

"I TRY NOT TO ARGUE WITH MY HORSE."

Q **I have an ex-racehorse who was retired due to a tendon injury and whom I, admittedly, mollycoddle! I bandage both legs at night and put magnet therapy tendon boots on during the day. And I'll turn him out when the weather's fine. But it's then that he gets excited – as he does when we're out hacking – and I have major battles in getting him to leave the yard. But I try not to argue with him as I worry that napping and dancing around will aggravate his tendon. I'm exasperated – what shall I do?**

A The problem is that because you are worried about pushing your horse to obey your commands, he is learning that your signals are unclear. He probably thinks that you do not really mean what you say, and that you're not going to force him to do something he doesn't want to.

Of course, you want to avoid any complications with his tendon problems, but you are helping him to develop behaviour problems that will make him unrideable anyway! It's only natural to commiserate with an animal who has been ill or had a hard life, but by failing to set limits right from the start, you are being equally unfair to your horse.

Setting the boundaries

In addition, remember that he must be able to learn his own limits too. If the vet thinks he is fit for work, then he is also fit to be in a field. Find him an old pony as a companion and turn him out in a small flat paddock until he settles into a routine. If you keep him cooped up for long periods, it's not surprising he reacts in an excitable way to having his freedom. All you can do is provide him with support bandages, place him in a safe environment and trust that he will learn his own limits.

You already know he is pushing you too far, but bear in mind that since he raced before you got him, it is likely that all of his exercise was done in the company of other horses. Therefore, it's quite understandable that he'd be reluctant to leave the stable yard and his companions. But most horses have to learn that this is something expected of them and by not making yourself clear to him that he must go forward when you ask him to, you are ensuring that he will always do this before a ride.

Ride out with another horse initially and work on motivating him to go forward on command, so that he is absolutely clear about your signals. Then you can work on sending him forward when in the yard and leaving the yard in stages, working up to doing this without the other horse and a human helper on the ground. Be firm and fair with him, and reward him with lots of praise for good behaviour.

Natalie Waran

Inseparable!

"MY SECOND HORSE IS PICKING UP HIS COMPANION'S BAD HABITS!"

Q **I desperately need help with my two rescued geldings. The first gelding I got, Jack, is very kind and gentle, but if he doesn't get his own way, or is left on his own, he is a complete nightmare, kicking down stable doors etc.**

Marvin, the second horse, we acquired more recently. He was fine when we first got him, but he seems to be picking up Jack's bad habits, and can be virtually unmanageable if separated from him.

A You mention that both your horses have come to you having been mistreated or neglected, and I feel that this does have a bearing on the problems that you are encountering. It is highly likely that their reluctance to leave one another is related to their need to maintain a stable social group (or in this case pair!).

In addition it does appear as if Marvin is starting to behave in a similar manner to Jack. Jack's behaviour is likely to have been formed over a long period of time, learning what he is capable of doing and the effect his behaviour has on humans and his surroundings (eg stable doors are easy for him to kick down), whereas I suspect that Marvin is currently learning his strength and capabilities.

Firstly we need to be clear that a fear of being left alone is not unusual. Horses are, after all, herd animals and so feel much safer in groups. Often without realising it, one of the main things that we have to teach horses from an early stage in their training, is to accept being alone as a normal and unthreatening event. This is obviously important for being able to ride out, compete etc. If the horse is not gradually accustomed to this early on in life, then it will often feel fearful when left alone later on.

I am afraid that by the sounds of it you are too late as far as Jack is concerned. He is older, very aware of his strength and is probably very determined about his needs! He sounds as

though he is a great character! You may need to cater to his whims by giving him a buddy (an older pony or donkey) that he can use to feel secure.

Marvin, however, can be trained to accept being alone, and this will need patience and consistent training. Once Jack stops creating whenever you are dealing with Marvin, I suspect that Marvin will be more willing to leave the yard and to hack out. You will need to gradually increase the distance between them when grooming perhaps, and then start to lead him away (use a bridle and a helper at first), and reward him with your voice and a section of apple, until he trusts you. Distract Jack with perhaps his feed and ensure that his buddy is in the next stable, during this time.

Once Marvin is away from Jack, I am confident that he will be able to enjoy your company; at the moment it sounds like he is only responding to Jack's insecurity.

Natalie Waran

Schooling a chunky horse

"MY CHUNKY HORSE KEEPS PULLING. "

Q My mare is only six, and when I backed her I used mild bits. However, as she has gained confidence, she has become more and more difficult to keep hold of, especially in canter when she seems to get carried away and just keeps pulling. I have tried lots of different bits, and currently ride her in an apple mouth pelham but feel it is heavy and unneccessary for such a young horse. She is only 14.3hh but over 450lbs and with a very muscular and thick neck. Any suggestions?

A Since you have already tried a wide range of bits without success, another change is unlikely to produce any improvement. It is more likely that the problems you have are more to do with schooling/riding technique than bitting.

As your mare is thick-set and heavy in front, she is probably tipping onto her forehand in canter and using you as a means of support. It is easier for her to go too fast than to shift her weight back onto her hocks and go in a more balanced way.

Try 'lifting' her front when you ask her to slow down, avoiding any backward pull on the reins which might encourage her to pull more

in return. This means raising your hands a little to raise her head and keeping your own weight back. If she is able to pull you forward, the problem will continue to get worse - your weight will be added to hers on the forehand.

There is much that can be done to improve the canter by schooling. Working on circles in an enclosed space will give you a chance to ride her forward in canter and thus teach her to engage her hindlegs better. Cantering on the lunge will help as well.

Most people spend ages schooling in trot and neglect the walk and canter, although it is more logical to try and work in all three gaits equally. If you school in canter in much the same way as you school in trot, I am sure you will soon see an improvement. A better canter in a schooling situation will lead to a better canter out hacking.

In a nutshell, if you can find a way of avoiding pulling and get the message of riding forward from your legs instead, your mare will start improving straight away.

Fliss Gillott

Melanomas - an alternative approach

"CAN I PREVENT THIS MELANOMA FROM GETTING WORSE?"

Q have a 21-year-old Welsh pony who has recently been diagnosed as having a melanoma. It does not appear to bother him, but I wonder if there is any herbal remedy I can give him to help prevent this melanoma from getting any worse?

I try to keep a strict check on his diet, feeding him Dengie Hi-Fi Lite and a pasture mix, as he has suffered from laminitis in the past. He also has a very thick coat but has tested negative to Cushing's Disease. Could these symptoms be linked to his melanoma?

A It is very good to have a confirmed diagnosis of such a lump, and, anatomically speaking, it may not increase in size for a number of years. However, melanomas can be produced in different parts of the body, and when they occur in any of the internal organs, eg the lungs, they cause substantial problems and the prognosis is very poor.

Thuja is one homoeopathic remedy which you may consider using in a high potency to reduce the size of the tumour, but malignant growths in older animals have to be taken very seriously and I think it is foolish to suggest that there might be some miracle cure.

Cushing's Disease

Cushing's Disease relates to the adrenal gland and the pituitary gland in the brain: it would not be impossible for the pony to develop Cushing's-like symptoms, but these would probably be a separate issue to the melanoma.

Your dietary management seems quite sound, and certainly the combination of Hi-Fi Lite and Pasture Mix seems to be appropriate for the older horse, although there are diets more suited to an ageing liver, if the pony develops any symptoms relating to reduced digestive function.

Poor liver function could be a feature of both developing melanomas or Cushing's. I can only underline that both homoeopathic and herbal remedies might give valuable support, if and when the pony shows any symptoms relating to the malignancy, but that, I'm afraid, is all they can do.

Sara Wyche

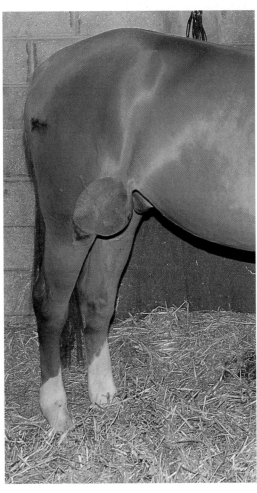

Frightened of water

"I DON'T WANT MY MARE'S FEAR OF WATER TO BE A PROBLEM WHEN SHE IS OLDER."

Q **Please could you advise me on how to get my three-year-old mare over her fear of water. I feel this must be done now so that it doesn't become a continuing problem when she is older.**

I have tried all sorts of things, such as spongeing water over her, but I don't want to make an issue of it and risk making her worse.

A This is a surprisingly common problem, with few horses willingly getting their feet wet without a very good reason. To them there is probably little sense in wading into the unknown - how can they be sure it is not either extremely deep or dangerously boggy? It is certainly cold and wet. If you look at it from the horse's point of view, it should be easier to understand your filly's reluctance to take the plunge.

Spongeing water over her will indeed get her used to the feel of water, but will it make her like the feel? I think not. A better angle would be to work on her obedience and trust in you as a leader. This level of obedience usually starts to build as a horse learns to work either on the lunge or under saddle.

Don't make an issue out of it

Going forward to voice or leg, not turning away from strange sights and sounds, but learning to work through these fears, and discovering that being obedient does not lead to harm but is a safe option - these things will be of much greater benefit. I would even go so far as to avoid water altogether until you have a greater rapport with her in other situations. Continuing to make an issue of going through water will only lead to her learning to be stubborn.

When the time is right, try to find a situation which involves crossing water, even if it is only a trickle across her path, because there is no alternative. This could be on the way home from a hack, or out to her field, wherever, as long as she feels it is worth getting to the other side. If there is a possibility of going round the water,

she will want to take it, in which case you may have a battle on your hands. This needs to be avoided.

Have an older horse there to give her a lead and be prepared to lead her yourself. With no fighting or hitting, be patient and wait for her to decide that she will have to go, even if it takes all day. Reward her as soon as she does it - she will be able to work out that you were right in saying it was safe and that it would have been easier to listen to you in the first place.

The only way you can speed things up a bit is by not letting her 'grow roots' by standing rooted to one spot. If she does, it will be too easy for her to switch off and let time pass pleasantly by. You could also make disturbing or irritating noises behind her which will make her side of the trickle less attractive than the other.

An alternative to this method is to take her somewhere so sloshy that she has to get her feet wet. If it proves to be a wet winter, this should not be a problem. However, this is not always an option with a three-year-old, as going out for a long enough and energetic enough hack to encourage her to drop her inhibitions and splash away could well be too much for her young legs.

A lot depends also on the type of soil you have in your area, as wet clay exerts such a pull that this is likely to be off putting rather than encouraging. The advantage of this method is that it is again making the object of getting wet less of an issue in itself and more a part of just being a riding horse and having fun. Riding out in a gang will help as part of this exercise. If your horse is out with bold and uninhibited others, she will be less likely to fuss about water round her feet and more concerned with staying with her friends.

Non-confrontational

Whichever method you use to get her started,

the main points to bear in mind are that you are as non-confrontational as possible, that she is learning general obedience first, and that you move on in small manageable stages which will not overface her. She will learn much more quickly if you create a situation in which she believes she has made the final choice as to how to carry out your orders.

Effectively, you are saying, "We have to get from here to there, how will we do it?", and she discovers that the only way just happens to be over water. The last thing you want so early in her career is for her to see water and immediately associate it with trauma. It is better if she associates it with a positive thought, in that she was brave and clever and you were terribly pleased with her.
Fliss Gillott